Patients' Emancipation: Towards Equality

Charlotte Williamson

isbn 978-1-912728-36-7

Set in twelve point Bembo. Page size 148mm x 210mm
printed litho on a one hundred gsm chosen for its sustainability.

Published and Printed by
Quacks Books
7 Grape Lane
Petergate
York YO1 7HU
01904 635967

To my husband Mark Williamson

and in memory of

Sir Donald Irvine

Contents

Preface

To understand the world is never a matter of simply recording our immediate impressions. Understanding inescapably involves reasoning. We have to 'read' what we feel and seem to see, and ask what these perceptions indicate and how we may take them into account without being overwhelmed by them.

Amartya Sen, economic philosopher, 2009, p viii.

When I first joined a patient group in the mid–1960s, and began to go round hospital wards with other members, I was puzzled by standards of care for patients. Why were they so variable, high in one ward, low in another in the same hospital? (I had read both patient groups' and professional groups' published sets of standards, so I had some knowledge to draw on.) How did consultants and ward sisters choose what standards of care they would have in their wards? Why did some accept the pleas of patient groups to change some specific standards while others rejected those pleas? Why, for that matter, did some patient groups seek improvements, as they defined them, to some standards and not to others? In the years that followed, I was fortunate to be appointed to various NHS advisory or provider bodies. Then I could think about these questions from inside these organisations, while taking part in their work and decision-making. The organisations included a community health council; a multidistrict health authority; a single district health authority, then a trust; patient liaison groups in three medical royal colleges in London. I was also a member of various government working parties, as well as of committees of the National Association of Health Authorities and of regional and local groups of various sorts. It was a privilege to have opportunities for observing these organisations and talking with many of their members and officers.

All the time, I felt I was doing a jigsaw puzzle with some of the pieces missing and no picture on the box to show me what that would be. But by the mid-2000s, I had discovered the missing pieces, from experience, discussion, and reading, and could fit them together to make a picture. I could put forward the theory that patients had developed an emancipation movement comparable to some other emancipation movements like the women's and the civil rights movements. The idea and the evidence for it I published in 2010, *Towards the Emancipation of Patients, Patients' experiences and the patient movement.*

Eleven years later, this book, *Patients' Emancipation: Towards Equality,* stands on its own. Some of the professional policies and practices that caused anguish to patients have gone; others remain or new ones have sprung up. Standards of patientcare can fall, especially in hard economic times or periods of social stress like the covid-19 pandemic. Managers and managerialism have become stronger politically since the 1980s and have affected health professionals and patients, sometimes for good, sometimes for ill.

My focus is on patients in general. People with mental health problems and people with learning disabilities have their own liberation (emancipation) movements, well written about in the academic and the popular press. My focus is also on patientcare in the UK and US. I have experienced their health services. And I find American writers on healthcare politics and medical sociology particularly illuminating.

The plan of the book is this: Chapter 1 sets the scene for the rest of the book, defining terms and describing situations that form the background to subsequent chapters. Chapter 2 traces the origins of the patients' emancipation movement and the development of the ideas and principles that guide it. Chapter 3 describes how patients develop different roles as some work to secure patients' emancipation. Chapter 4 is about doctors, particularly those who are allies of patients in opposing coercive or oppressive policies and practices. Chapter 5 is about managers and managerialists. Chapter 6 draws on political theory to explain some of the subtle ways, often unrecognised by patients and by doctors, through which patients' interests in their own autonomy are threatened. The last chapter, Chapter 7, ends with hope for eventual equality of esteem, of voice, and of power between patients, doctors, and managers. Equality is the end sought by the patients' emancipation movement, however far away it seems.

Acknowledgements

I am immensely grateful to all those with whom I worked in local and national statutory and voluntary bodies. I also thank with pleasure the many patients, patient activists, doctors, nurses, midwives, and managers who have talked with me, frankly and eloquently, some over many years.

Especially I thank those who have read and commented on some or all of the book's chapters. Their current or recent roles are included with their names. They are Rob Baggott, professor of public policy; Mitzi Blennerhassett, patient activist; Heather Goodare, patient activist; Gerry Jackson, GP; David Hunter, professor of health policy and management; David Misselbrook, GP and professor of family medicine; Catti Moss, GP and clinical professor of medical education; Andrew Smith, professor of anaesthesia; Helen Williams, consultant pathologist; Patricia Wilkie, patient activist; Mark Williamson, professor of biology; Stephen Yorston, director of finance at an NHS trust.

I also record my gratitude to those no longer with us: Donald Irvine, GP; Ann Johnson, consultant surgeon and oncologist; Peter Kennedy, consultant psychiatrist and chief executive at an NHS trust; David Wilkinson, consultant radiologist.

My grateful thanks, too, to Katy Midgley and Martin Nelson at Quacks Books, York for their cordial efficiency.

My nephew, Andrew Mitchell, gave me invaluable advice on technical matters.

Ideas about emancipation and about standards of care are often controversial and can arouse deep feelings in us all. Thinking about the oppression of patients is painful. But the company, the conversation, and the friendship of so many people have brought me joy.

Chapter 1

Introduction to patients' emancipation

[professional] cultural attitudes ... which regard the patient as an entity to be managed, but not necessarily to be listened to as a person.

Sir Ian Kennedy, medical ethicist, 2006, p 27.

Introduction

This chapter sets the scene for the rest of the book. It defines emancipation and its companions, interests and power. It gives an example of a sequence of emancipatory actions by patients and by maternity care staff over almost 50 years, from the late 1950s to the early 2000s. The chapter then compares the patients' emancipation movement with the women's and civil rights movements. Whether people like or dislike, welcome or fear, these social movements, they are familiar and accepted, while the patients' emancipation movement is still relatively unfamiliar. Lastly, the chapter discusses some everyday examples of oppressive professional practices that can cause distress to patients, who feel they are not being treated 'as people'. I focus mainly on doctors, as the most powerful group in patientcare, though other health professionals, managers, and policy-makers also play parts in oppressing and in emancipating patients.

Patients' emancipation defined

Until recently, the idea of the emancipation of patients was new and strange. It is no longer new. But it can still seem strange: historically patients have not been seen as a category of people who are institutionally disadvantaged or oppressed. Emancipation is a political term, a metaphor from long-ago Romans freeing their slaves. We don't know how many slaves tried to free themselves from the fetters that deprived them of freedom. But we do know that since the late 1950s and early 1960s, some patients have tried to secure changes to healthcare policies and practices that would remove or lessen constraints on their freedom to act as they thought right. Emancipation is a useful metaphor because it points to healthcare professionals, as well as to patients themselves, trying to set free patients from unnecessary constraints on their freedom and autonomy. Just as some patients try to change policies and practices in emancipatory ways and other are content with the status quo, so some health professionals work in emancipatory ways and others do not.

Emancipation can be defined as setting people free from control and constraint, actual or metaphorical (Brown, 1993). Metaphorical controls and constraints include coercions and threats to people's autonomy and to their opportunities for choosing their own courses of action (self-determination). Doctors or other health professionals may coerce patients within the doctor-patient relationship; institutions may have coercive policies; society may permit unjust coercions. Emancipatory actions or emancipatory standards must include this setting free element: high standards (standards that both professionals and patients agree are good) without that element, though desirable, are not necessarily emancipatory.

Power and interests

Emancipation is a political idea; it has to do with power. Power is the ability to get things done as best suits the interests of those who hold it (Lukes, 2005). Interests are the stakes that people have in things they value (Lukes, 2005). Patients and doctors both have stakes in the quality of healthcare, in their clinical relationships, and in their own autonomy. Doctors collectively have more power than patients. If power were equal, patients would not need to take emancipatory actions.

Differences in power between doctors and patients were usually accepted in the early 20th century as Medicine became ever more successful at treating diseases (Freidson, 1970). Society's approval of Medicine (the term means medical science and the profession's beliefs and actions); its relationships with the state; and the relationships between doctors as a social group and patients as a social group settled into what sociologists call 'social structures'. Social structures are the political, legal, economic, cultural beliefs, and institutions that hold societies together (Sharrock and Watson, 1995). Social structures come to be taken for granted as 'natural'. They provide security and predictability. They limit people's freedoms and opportunities to change society. But they do not stop them completely; opportunities remain or can be created. Social life depends on the interplays of power, the social structure, and the people who choose to take actions, within those limitations and opportunities (Lukes, 2005). If those people's actions succeed, they can change social structures. New patterns of relationships and of every-day actions replace the old ones.

Here is an example of a series of emancipatory actions. It is taken from the past because that can show some things more clearly than contemporary instances: there is an end as well as a beginning and emotions, felt so keenly at the time, have died down.

Today, every woman who gives birth to her baby in a hospital in the UK is free to have her partner with her. Her partner, or someone else whom she chooses, can stay with her before, during and after the birth. Her partner or companion can keep her company, support her with touch and with words, and welcome the new baby into the world. Only if an unexpected difficulty or an emergency arise, may the partner or companion be asked to wait briefly outside the room. Everyone takes this for granted now. But in the 1950s, women and their partners were allowed to be with each other only in the early stages of labour, if at all, and then only during the hospital's brief 'visiting times'. By the mid-1960s, the partner was allowed in some hospitals, though not in others, to stay for the birth itself, provided doctors did not use instruments such as obstetric forceps to deliver the baby. But the partner or companion was only allowed to stay if the midwives thought the woman and the partner or companion were 'suitable'. (Private patients and doctors' wives or husbands were more suitable than other people.) By the 1980s, partners were allowed to be present for deliveries when obstetric instruments were used. By the 1990s, partners could be present for planned Caesarean operations carried out if the woman were given regional anaesthesia and so was conscious. By the 2000s, the partner could sometimes be present for a Caesarean carried out under general anaesthesia while the woman was unconscious (Williamson, 2010).

These changes can be looked at in two ways. From one perspective, they were gradual improvements made by obstetricians and midwives in the last half of the 20th Century. The changes made childbirth more comfortable, gave constant companionship and support to the woman, and made a propitious start to the new baby's family life. But from another perspective, this was not a smooth professional progression from good care to better care. It was a battle ground. Each change, each new removal of coercion from the woman and her partner, each new freedom for them to be together, had to be fought for by maternity care patient pressure groups – chiefly the National Childbirth Trust (NCT), founded in 1956, and the Association for Improvements in the Maternity Services (AIMS), founded in 1960. Their members, and other women influenced by the grapevine and by the press, had innumerable pleading meetings with obstetricians and midwives. The national groups provided their local branches with research papers and data, so their members could be well-informed and confident in pressing for changes to policies. Pregnant women made repeated requests to have their partners present; suffered anxiety lest they be refused; and felt anguish and anger when they were. Almost as much distress was caused to midwives and obstetricians. They were sometimes upset, dismayed or angry when women made these requests. They often resisted them. Even within the same maternity unit, individual obstetricians and individual midwives could hold different views. (Pregnant women could hold different views, too; but as emancipatory policies give patients freedom to choose, that didn't matter.) Conflict and discord were country-wide.

These changes from coercions to freedoms are easy to follow now. But the exact parts played by obstetricians, by midwives, by pressure groups, and by individual pregnant women varied from place to place. Society's expectations changed, too, as women, obstetricians, and midwives wrote articles in professional and lay journals and in the wider press. Social change depends ultimately on individuals. They build on the ideas and on the work of those before them and of those around them, wherever those ideas came from originally. Taking action to oppose powerful groups or individuals requires energy, confidence, and courage – forms of personal and political power. But a little bread on the water can feed a lot of fishes.

The wider social setting and other emancipation movements

Emancipation movements disrupt society and many people oppose them, especially in their early stages. Comparing the patients' emancipation movement with the women's and the civil rights movements shows this.

Medicine can free people from the dangers of some diseases and from the pains or disabilities of others. It can even free people from the fear of disease. Seventy years ago, prudent parents forbade their children to go to the cinema or the public swimming pool in summer lest they catch polio. Now vaccination protects us all from this crippling and fatal disease. Medicine can often enable people to live their lives as if there had been no interruptions from sickness or accident. These are achievements we value. During the 2020 covid-19 virus pandemic, doctors and other healthcare professionals showed great altruism and devotion to their work; and the whole of the UK population admired and felt grateful to them. But doctors have not ensured that their policies, practices, and assumptions respect patients' sense of their own personhood, capabilities, responsibilities, and autonomy. When Medicine reached the height of its power in the 1950s and 1960s, some patients begin to oppose or resist what they saw as its harmful practices. Looking back, we can see that those patients who took action started an emancipation movement. As they opposed policies and practices in different medical specialities, an emancipatory pattern was not at first evident (Chapter 2).

Patients are people in current clinical relationships with clinicians. It is the clinical relationship that defines patients. Patients may or may not be ill, injured, at the onset of a new disability, or at an acute worsening of an old disability. Many patients, notably GPs' patients, are well. Doctors sometimes behave towards well patients as if they were ill. This probably contributes to well patients taking actions that we can see as emancipatory.

The 'patient movement' is the term for patients and patient groups that work for patients' interests. Some work for patients' interests that match or support doctors' interests. Pressing for more staff, for more money for effective treatments, for more convenient buildings, benefit doctors as well as patients. Other patients and patient groups work for patients' interests, as these patients and patient groups define them, that can conflict with doctors' interests as doctors define them. Doctors have interests in their working conditions, money earned, work schedules, and so on, like all who do paid work. These may or may not fit with patients' interests; and patients usually accept doctors' interests here. Much more importantly, doctors tend to believe that they know what patients' interests are. That belief lies at the heart of conflicts between them and patients. Challenging it and persuading doctors that they ought to change their policies and practices to meet patients' definitions of their interests, makes the emancipatory part of the patient movement (Williamson, 2010). Because doctors commit themselves to acting for the good of their patients and in their patients' interests, who decides what those interests are and whether and how they should be met is crucial pragmatically and politically.

We rely on doctors to give us clinical care when we need it. Doctors are part of the security that the state provides for its citizens, whatever the financial arrangements between doctors, patients, and the state. We count on this security; and the value we put on doctors can make the idea of a patient emancipation movement seem strange. Familiar emancipation movements like the women's movement or the civil rights movement may seem not to fit patients and doctors. Certainly, patients' emancipation is different from those emancipation movements in some ways. But it is like them in others. Here I compare first the similarities, then differences.

Similarities between the patients' emancipation movement, the women's and the civil rights movements

1. Long before the beginnings of a new emancipation movement, members of the more powerful group take their own power for granted. If they think about it at all, they think that their own superior merits justify their power: their skin white not coloured;

their bodies male not female; their bodies strong not weak; their health good not bad. Moreover, powerful social groups attribute characteristics to weaker groups that justify or provide reasons for their domination of them (Fuchs Epstein, 1988). In particular, members of the more powerful, dominant group often see themselves as having better intellects and greater moral insight and sense of responsibility.

Novels show this well. For women's inferiority, try 19th Century British novels by Trollope, Mrs Gaskell or George Eliot. 'It doesn't signify what [women] think – they are not called on to judge or to act,' says Harold Transome to his mother in *Felix Holt*, 1866 (George Eliot, 1999, p 33). For blacks' inferiority, read *The Help*, a novel depicting life in the 1960s in Jackson, Mississippi, by the white American, Kathryn Stockett, published in 2009. There a black maid laments '…that moment … that comes in every white child's life when they start to think that colored folks ain't as good as whites' (Stockett, 2009, p 96). For non-fiction, try *Negroland*, a contemporary memoir by the American Negro, Margo Jefferson. She notes that in her childhood, children were warned that '…most whites would be glad to see [black people] returned to indigence, deference and subservience' (Jefferson, 2015, p 3). (I use the terms these American writers used. In the UK today, the acceptable terms for people of colour are black, Asian or minority ethnic – BAME for short. 'Black' and 'white' are problematic terms, but are currently favoured in popular culture, for example, the Black Lives Matter movement, and in serious journalism, for example *The Economist*.)

Doctors' sense of their superiority to patients, and dominance over them, is hidden by rhetoric and often by doctors' good manners. They may rise and shake your hand when you enter their consulting room, just as well-mannered men rise for women or for older men. But doctors' use of language can give them away. They write of 'managing' the patient, as if patients were always unconscious or lacked mental capacity. Patients' requests are called 'demands' as if they were all selfish or unreasonable. This is familiar jargon, if distasteful to patients. But GPs have taken recently to referring to their interactions with patients as 'the coalface', even in journals that patients can read (for an example see Hayden and Lakhani, 2019). That can hit patients when they come across it. Is this what my nice doctor really thinks of me? Grim, grimy, dangerous? Later in this chapter, examples of how doctors speak to patients illustrate a pattern of the stronger interest-holders speaking to the weaker in ways that the stronger think harmless or benevolent and the weaker feel contempt for or resent. This is probably a common pattern, in spite of 'political correctness' that reminds people to speak sensitively to or about members of disadvantaged groups.

Some doctors are well aware of doctors' dominant power and of the harm it can do. The British GP, Professor David Misselbrook, uses a military metaphor, with doctors as officers and patients as private soldiers, to point out dominance's threat to patients' autonomy (Misselbrook, 2001). He does not suggest mutiny. But his imagery does. The endocrinologist at Mayo Clinic in the US, Dr Victor Montori, says that doctors can be cruel to patients, thinking them 'not like us, not our kin' but as 'a suffering and dependent subspecies …with 'nothing in common with our humanity' (Montori, 2017 p 15). He urges doctors and patients to 'revolt' for kinder and more caring care, with healthy people and patients who are well enough to act, leading the way.

2. Some members of the weaker social group begin to see harms to themselves, and to people like them, in the more powerful group's customary attitudes and behaviours. They analyse these harms. They try to get members of the stronger groups to change their ways. In the early days of the American civil rights movement, following the emancipation of slaves in 1863, some of the harms that continued from the days of slavery were so evident they hardly needed to be uncovered. Others gradually became apparent as society and as people's expectations changed. Women, black, Asian and minority ethnic people, and patients continue to see new harms. The example from childbirth illustrates this. Seeing and naming (identifying) one new harm leads to identifying others, just as a naturalist learns to identify different species of mosses and grasses through study and practice.

3. Members of the weaker group reject the idea that members of the stronger group are morally or intellectually superior to them. They begin to work for independence of thought. They try to secure autonomy, defined as freedom from coercion, especially in making decisions, for themselves and for fellow members of their group (Williamson, 1992). They seek equality of worth and of voice with members of the more powerful group. The American feminist writer, Carolyn Heilbrun, defines power as *the ability to take one's place in whatever discourse is essential to action and the right to have one's part matter* (Heilbrun, 1989, p 18). She was thinking of discourses between individual people. But it also applies to discourses between groups, where more powerful groups can push to the side (marginalise) weaker groups or their views.

4. Members of the more powerful group resist changes to the status quo that would give more power to the weaker group at the expense of their own. They are likely to resist ideas of equality of power and of human worth, and of intellectual and moral capabilities. They can show displeasure when a member of the weaker group tries to converse on equal terms or ventures – or strays - into matters the stronger group member considers inappropriate. In Jane Austen's *Emma,* 1816, only men discussed the weather, although women in their thin shoes and long dresses were exposed to it, too . Doctors may not say that they look down on patients. But some doctors' actions speak for them. (Examples later in this chapter.)

Differences between the patents' emancipation movement and the women's and civil rights movements

1. Doctors are committed to acting for the good of their patients. That is enshrined in their beliefs about their own moral status and ethical behaviour (Pellegrino and Thomasma, 1981). Doctors hold these beliefs sincerely. They re-state them from time to time (Royal College of Physicians, 2005). They try to act on them and they feel uneasy when they cannot. (Doctors' and other health professionals' unease when they are prevented from doing the right thing for their patients by institutional constraints that they cannot change is called 'moral distress', Oliver, 2018; and Chapter 6). Men and white people are not committed to acting for the good of women or of black, Asian or minority ethnic people.

2. Patients are grateful for the good that doctors do; for their clinical skills and expertise; and for their kindness and help in the

universal vicissitudes of sickness, accident, disability, and death. Men and white people can do good things for patients, but not usually those that depend on medical training and experience.

3. Being a patient is, for most people, most of the time, a temporary state. They can tolerate brief uneasy clinical relationships and minor hardships. People with long term or recurrent diseases or with permanent disabilities still generally have only temporary episodes of active clinical relationships. Being a doctor is, once achieved, a permanent state. Even if a doctor gives up his or her registration, the medical mind-set remains.

4. Being a doctor is always a matter of choice. Being a patient is sometimes or partly a matter of choice. People may decide not to see a doctor when they feel ill. (My father used to say 'I don't feel well enough to go to the doctor.') But under some circumstances, patients can be obliged to enter into clinical relationships and compelled to accept clinical advice. If they are, strict legal provisions and rights of appeal safeguard them and their interests (Williamson, 1991.)

5. Doctors can become patients and patients can become doctors. But doctors are more likely to become patients than patients are to become doctors.

Conclusion from these comparisons

For many people, dissimilarities between the unfamiliar idea of patients' emancipation and the familiar ideas of well-known emancipation movements are more important than the similarities.

13

The dissimilarities reassure them. They can look kindly, even admiringly on doctors, even though they know that doctors may fail to act according to their ethical principles and that their view of their interests is not always the same as their own. And they know (if they read newspapers) that doctors sometimes ignore up-to-date clinical knowledge, make wrong diagnoses, and may be rationing treatments. Doctors' shortcomings can remind people that doctors are human and prone to error, like themselves. Doctors' accounts of their experiences and hardships, and of their concern for their patients, can be deeply touching, even heart-breaking, as Dr Rachel Clarke eloquently describes (Clarke, 2017). But so can patients' accounts of their experiences. How then do patients and doctors see each other?

How patients and doctors see each other

Before doctors' rise to power in the early and mid-20th century, middle-class patients were often economically and socially superior to doctors. Patients depended on advice and help from their doctors but were not less powerful than they were. Mrs Gaskell, a skilful social commentator, shows this in her novels. But since doctors' collective rise to power, patients individually and collectively have been less powerful (Alford, 1975). Patients' lack of power can be seen in the American sociologist, Talcott Parsons', descriptions of patients' and doctors' ideal behaviours (Parsons, 1951). He held that:

Patients should relinquish their normal responsibilities; be relieved of their normal duties; obey their doctors' instructions; and wish to get well. Doctors reciprocally should be competent;

act objectively; have their patients' welfare at heart; and be uninfluenced by commercial or personal considerations.

Allowing for obvious differences in circumstances, the description for patients would have fitted women and slaves in the early and mid-19th Century. A married women had to relinquish her money to her husband; he was responsible for her welfare and for the custody of their children; and in her marriage vows, she had promised to obey him. Slaves' masters had responsibility for their welfare; could sell them or separate them from their spouses and children; required obedience; and saw that after illness, they returned to work in the cotton or sugar fields or homestead. Husbands and slave owners had a good deal of freedom to act as they pleased within the law it as stood at the time. After the abolition of slavery, white people in the south hardly changed their views of black people's inferiority. Many gave political and practical support to white supremacy (Zinn, 2010).

Parson's thesis was highly influential. It entered into medical thinking on both sides of the Atlantic, not surprisingly since it supported doctors' power so strongly. Although the theory is no longer wholly accepted by social scientists, they still discuss it at length, as relevant though imperfect (Starr, 2000). Today, the depiction of patients would seem bizarre at best, at worst, damaging. But remnants of it linger on in the relationships between doctors and patients. From the earliest days of the patient movement, and probably long before, patients have complained of two traits in doctors: that doctors did not always treat them 'as people'; and that they often showed a paternalistic 'we know what is best for you' attitude.

Patients 'as people'

Being a person means, in western societies, an autonomous person, self-determining to the extent that he or she wants to be and can: this includes choosing dependence on others, again to the extent that he or she wants to and can. Autonomous means free from imposed overt or covert coercions (Jensen and Mooney, 1990). Medical ethics requires doctors to respect patients' autonomy (Beauchamp and Childress, 2009). But some doctors pay little attention to it. Perhaps they do not take patients' autonomy seriously; or do not understand its implications for their own day-to-day practice; or decide they don't have enough time for it (Ives et al., 2018). 'Not enough time' has replaced 'risks of infection' as a hold-all explanation for not doing what patients want or what professional standards decree. Both explanations were and are partly true. Both could be put right if the political will and the resources were there.

Patients' sense that some doctors do not treat them 'as people' or 'as a person' comes directly from those doctors' behaviour towards them. People can have good relationships with one another yet harbour thoughts and feelings that each keeps private from the other, as in a happy marriage. But all communications between people can let slip their 'real' feelings. Clues that the doctors let fall – their body language, manner, words – can give the impression that they don't see the patient as a person. Patients see themselves as people first, as patients second. Many doctors see the patient first, the person second or, as patients complain, not at all. Doctors' words, remembered and recounted to friends, are especially telling. Here are instances from patients' indignant or derisive accounts, spontaneously told to me soon after they happened, with their dates.

16

Patients can feel belittled by lack of basic courtesy, like doctors not introducing themselves before carrying out a major abdominal operation (2013) or a Caesarean section (2018) on conscious patients, or before giving them important information or advice (2013). Patients can feel patronised, if addressed as 'my dear' or by their first names without their permission (2017). They can feel insulted by baby-talk, like 'food tube' for oesophagus or 'water-works' for the urinary system (2013). Besides, these terms are puzzling. 'Food pipe' could be any part of the gut from top to bottom. 'Waterworks' could be kidneys, ureter, bladder, and so on. Doctors assume that patients don't know the correct terms and, instead of offering them, they reinforce patients' lack of knowledge. Or patients can feel mortified if their questions are fielded back contemptuously. Patient, 'What are my eye pressures?' Ophthalmologist, 'If I told you, you wouldn't understand the figures' (2018). Patient, 'What about side effects?' GP, 'When did you get a medical degree?' (2019). Patient, 'How do you know that I'm free of this disease?' Consultant, 'Don't you trust me?' (2019).

Behaviours like these contributed to patients setting up patient pressure groups in the 1960s. (The original name for the Association for Improvements in the Maternity Services (AIMS) was the Society for the Prevention of Cruelty to Pregnant Women.) They anger patients, distract them from what the doctor is saying, and make them doubt the doctor's competence. (If doctors can't even say their own names, what else can't they do?) As a patient with cancer said in 1988 'I do not want to enter the surgery and leave my personhood and capacities outside the door. How then can I use my resources to aid my recovery?' (Jolley, 1988).

We all sometimes say ill-considered things. The relevance of these examples to oppression and emancipation is their persistence and the distress they cause patients. They perhaps reflect these doctors' unconscious attempts to push patients back into an inferior and subservient 'patient role' on the Parsons' model. Or they may reflect doctors' wish to control medical knowledge, the basis of medical power (Salter, 2004). As patients become better informed through the internet (no more trips to the public library in icy winter), ask more questions, and take more responsibility for their own health, such responses will sadden anyone who cares about doctors as well as about patients.

How far doctors consciously intend these put-downs and whether they are aimed at patients' personhoods or at their abilities and expertises (their capacities) has long been puzzling. But recently, an explanation has been put forward from inside the medical profession itself.

Dame Clare Gerada, a former president of the Royal College of General Practitioners, and her son, an anthropologist, say that at medical school, doctors learn to think of themselves as being special and different from patients: they come to believe that they, unlike patients, do not become ill. This is a defence mechanism against the pain and horror of daily contact with disease, suffering, and death. Feelings of being different from patients help doctors feel invulnerable and able to carry on with looking after patients (Wessely and Gerada, 2013). This explanation is borne out by psychoanalytic research into nursing. It found that in nursing, the anxieties caused by close continuous contact with individual patient's distress were avoided by splitting nursing into tasks carried out by different nurses (Menzies Lyth, 1988). This splitting is not so easy for doctors who have to concentrate on individual patients and their predicaments. Doctors, like other people, need defences against overwhelming anxiety. Lay people's defences are probably mostly just not thinking much about illness and death, at least when they are young. Doctors cannot do that.

Doctors see themselves, correctly, as having legitimate authority, their clinical and professional power granted by the state (Klein, 1989). Doctors' feelings of being different, combined with greater power, can easily turn into feelings of superiority towards patients and even towards lay (non-medical) people who are not ill. So patients' sense that their doctors regard themselves as superior to them is soundly-based, at least for some patients and for some doctors.

Experienced patients can remind doctors that patients are people, not just patients. Here are instances from patients' accounts, told to me with a sense of achievement. They can leave a highbrow novel or journal casually open on their bed (1996); mention that they are due to give a seminar at a famous university (2018); refer to another doctor by his or her first and last names without the title 'Dr'; say they are friends of the consultant – 'our children go to the same school' (2017); use technical terms like 'spontaneous abortion' instead of 'miscarriage' (2016); and hold out their hand to shake the doctor's (1960). The effects of these actions can be miraculous. It's as if the patient's behaving 'as a person' sets the doctor free to be a person, too. A more cordial and more equal relationship with more exchange of information and easier shared decision-making can follow. The patient can feel rewarded. Perhaps so can the doctor.

Even for well-educated, professional people like those above, being a confident, articulate patient takes hard work. Only if you happen to be of high social status; important in the doctor's social or professional network; a member of a health service organisation like a trust board; or a private patient, is it likely to be a little easier.

'Doctors know best'

The second common lament of patients, that doctors behave as if 'we know what is best for you' is also complicated. Doctors know more about clinical medicine than most non-doctors. Patients respect that. But patients do not always think that their doctors know what is best for them. Doctors learn at medical school to adopt a confident, authoritarian manner. They believe that patients want that and feel reassured by it (Wessely and Gerada, 2013). Some patients are reassured (Gray, 2002). Others are not. But patients sometimes think it prudent to seem to accept their doctors' advice while privately deciding to reject it (Chapter 3). Doctors perhaps confuse patients' hopes for clinical competence, and their relief when they meet it, with their apparent acceptance of what their doctors say. Patients set great store on doctors' competence. They compare doctors' competences when they talk with friends or with strangers in hospitals or GPs' surgeries. 'Is he/she any good?' are usually the words spoken by people in all social classes. Readers have probably used them. These everyday observations have been echoed by social science research (Bury, 2004).

Patients' experiences, views, and judgements about their doctors' clinical competence often seem to be regarded by doctors as matters into which patients must not stray (Chisholm et al., 2006). Official questionnaires tend to omit it. The Care Quality Commission monitors, inspects, and regulates hospital and GP services in England and Wales. A recent questionnaire to GPs' patients asked them about their GPs' appointments system, home visits, if they were given options for place of treatment, and other questions about their doctors' style (CQC, 2019). It did not ask whether their GPs' diagnoses or referrals had turned out to be correct or if their treatments had been effective. In patientcare, as in the rest of life, what is not said or not asked can be more important than what is – a political truism.

Conclusion

Social structures form the background to our lives; but we live our lives and take our actions personally, as people in relationships with other people. Each new generation of doctors and patients has to live with the social structures it inherits from its predecessors' ways of thinking and behaving. Each new generation is not responsible for the attitudes, policies, and practices it inherits. It need feel no guilt about them. (I make this point because once doctors become aware of the harms their past practices could have done, they can feel uneasy.) But both patients and doctors can try to set in train changes. The patients' emancipation movement is not a revolution nor a mutiny: its members do not seek to overthrow or to harm doctors. Rather, they want them to change some of their policies and practices to take patients' interests, as patients define them, into account. That doesn't seem a lot to ask. But the following chapters show that it often is.

Chapter 2

Patients take action: ideas and principles

...the door was open to vistas that would have seemed too glaring before.

Hans Toch, social psychologist, 1965, p 238.

Introduction

This chapter starts with an account of the beginning and early stages of the patient emancipation movement. It then describes how patient groups worked and still work. Lastly, it outlines the creation of the patient emancipation movement's principles, the set of ideas that guide and explain its members' beliefs and actions. As patients developed these ideas, they began to develop new roles. Ideas and roles affect each other: they are closely intertwined. But for clarity, discussion of these new roles is in the next chapter.

The patient emancipation movement's early stages

After the second world war, a shift in widely accepted sets of values seems to have taken place across Europe and North America, weakening people's faith or trust in authority. (Something similar may take place after the covid-19 pandemic.) By the late 1950s and early 1960s, new social groups to 'do something about' problems like child poverty, homelessness, and poor healthcare sprang up and flourished in the UK (Curtis and Sanderson, 2004).Voluntary (that is, unpaid) groups for healthcare included pressure groups for higher standards of patientcare; support groups to raise more resources for health professionals' work; self-help groups whose members gave each other information and emotional support; single issue or single disease groups; and groups combining these aims. Most of the pressure groups working for higher standards of care defined 'higher' as those that freed patients from coercions, like those in the childbirth example in the last chapter. But the idea of emancipation for patients was not yet even a distant vista.

The beginnings of what will become an emancipation movement are often hard to trace. People tell stories of hardships or cruelties. They put forth ideas that at first seem strange. But the ideas begin to make sense when they are joined to the stories. Individual people's words can have lasting influence. But bringing about effective social change usually requires social action, action by groups of people. Groups of just a few people can take action with no aim beyond setting right what they see as a wrong. They can act long before they foresee what their actions will mean. Actions create meanings. Meanings guide further actions. What would once have seemed unthinkable begins to be thought about. One of the doors that led to opening up the vista of the civil rights movement in the US turned out to be vocational training for impoverished former slaves (Toch, 1965). The emancipatory part of the patient movement shows the same pattern: specific actions lead to unforeseen and sometimes momentous social changes, like sowing a bean seed and getting a beech tree.

Patients or their parents in the UK in the late 1950s and early 1960s began to oppose doctors', midwives', and nurses' policies and practices that they thought harmed their children, themselves or other patients. They found people who, like them, believed that they could take action to oppose those harms. This is how small groups opposing larger, more powerful, groups start (Mansbridge, 2001). These relatives and adult patients formed pressure groups to work for changes to policies, practices, and standards of treatment and care. They began to identify patients' values and definitions of their interests. Those interests sometimes conflicted, sometimes coincided, with the medical profession's interests. Interests bring us back to power, Chapter 1, which ever gleams behind emancipation movements.

Patient pressure groups founded by the parents of children in hospital and of children with learning disabilities or by people with mental illness or physical disabilities, were started at about the same time. A common factor was probably their founding members' good health; they were not preoccupied with or incapacitated by bodily illness and its anxieties. Some early NCT and AIMS members were members of the women's movement or influenced by it. But not all were.

Members of these groups called themselves patient representatives or patient advocates or consumerists. Activists, a term used by sociologists and political scientists, seems to me better. The groups are patient activist groups, the individuals, patient activists.

The harm is usually felt as an affront to the self, to its moral, psychological or physical being (Mansbridge, 2001). The affront can spark a damascene moment, an instantaneous conversion from one set of beliefs to another, as St Paul was converted from being a Pharisee to a being a Christian on the road from Jerusalem to Damascus in AD 33. People converted can often remember the exact place and time when it happened. For feminists, the conversion is from belief that women are not discriminated against to belief that they are. For patient activists, the conversion is from belief in the dedication of doctors to their patients' interests to belief in doctors' potential to act against their patients' interests (Chapter I). The conversion to patient activism is usually intensely personal, though reading about or hearing others' experiences can also prompt it.

At first, patient activists' reactions were passionate responses to one or a few specific harms: children's wards in hospitals that prevented parents from being with their sick babies and young children; maternity wards that insisted that mothers feed their newborn babies, not when each baby and mother decided, but at times each ward sister favoured; lack of warning to patients about treatments' side effects that, in the event, affected them. Patient activist groups came to see health professionals' and institutions' actions like these as harmful restrictions and coercions that violated patients' or parents' responsibilities to themselves, to their dependents or to their communities. (Hospital staff saw them as customary good practice. Everyone likes to believe that what they are doing is good, and much that staff did was good.) Members of patient activist groups often joined other patient activist groups, and told them about what they were doing and thinking. (These were pre-internet days.)

As activist groups got going, members compared their intuitions and experiences, drew out meanings from them, and analysed the harms. In the women's movement this is called 'consciousness raising' (Tong, 2009). In patient activism, it is called 'creating new knowledge'. Members add knowledge from other sources to their experiential and intuitive knowledge to create new ways of seeing and understanding things, new perceptions and perspectives (Thomas, 2002). They take knowledge from various sources: 'radical' health professionals (sometimes unpopular with their colleagues, Chapter 4); clinical medicine; social and natural sciences; medical ethics; and the law. They add to and take from the zeitgeist, the common knowledge, feelings and ways of behaving that mark societies. Activists sometimes are able to draw on diverse fields of knowledge more freely than some professionals can (Williams and Popay, 2006). Patient activists' emotional alignment with patients helps them pick up knowledge that fits that alignment, like picking up some shells but not others on a seashore.

Intuitions and experiences are important in patient activism. Intuition is the immediate apperception of an idea or a situation without conscious reasoned thought, often accompanied by a rush of feeling (Brown, 1993). It does not depend entirely on feelings and sensitivities. It depends also on knowledge and experience. 'I feel strongly and I think strongly: but I seldom feel without thinking or think without feeling', wrote the poet Samuel Taylor Coleridge (Coleridge, 1796). Early patient activists drew on their feelings and on ordinary social values and norms in order to challenge hospital routines for newborn babies and sick children. But they drew on knowledge for arguing with health professionals. They used DW Winnicott's and John Bowlby's popular psychoanalytic writings about the parent-child relationship (Winnicott, 1964; Bowlby, 1965). Their books were widely read by the public. Patient activists, like other reformers, use what opportunities the social structures of their day offer – here these psychoanalytic writings.

How patient activist groups work

Patients' experiences are the raw material and the inspiration for patient activism. But citing those experiences on their own seldom changes professional practices. Medicine is a rational and scientific subject. It usually has to be countered on its own terms. Patients' experiences have to be interpreted and reinforced by evidence and argument that doctors, trained academically, can accept. It's easy to talk of marrying the perspectives of patients and doctors. But doctors are likely to give more weight to their perspectives than to patients'. And they usually need evidence of the harms their established policies and practices do, before they will change them.

Patient activists think a lot about standards of treatment and care. Standards are the currency of patientcare, as money is the currency of commerce and fruit and vegetables of green-grocers. Standards are prescriptive descriptions of specific actions to which qualitative or quantitative values are applied (Williamson, 1987). ('Take patients' blood pressure every 4 hours and ask their permission first', is an example.) Which actions to single out from the innumerable actions health professionals take every day and what values to apply to them, is often controversial. So patient activists check what standards are in place in the patientcare they are concerned with; check whether staff comply with them; and consider whether the standards are right as they judge that. If dissatisfied, they can try to gain acceptance for different standards. They can do nothing about standards that are secret within institutions – until they discover them.

Patient activists' actions often fell, and still fall, into a pattern. First, patients may identify harms from a medicine, procedure or policy more quickly than health professionals do: it is patients not professionals who experience those harms. Patient activists learn of the harms; examine them; and assemble relevant 'new knowledge' including its scientific components. Then they can press for changes more quickly than professionals can, for professionals are often bound by inhibitions and customs in their organisations (Chapter 6).

Examples of patient activist groups that worked, and still work, this way include:

AIMS, the Association for Improvements in the Maternity Services, founded in 1960, opposes the routine use in childbirth of inflexible clinical protocols that are appropriate for some women but damaging for others. AIMS judges some aspects of maternity care as bad or worse than they were seventy years ago (Murphy-Lawless, 2016).

RAGE, the Radiation Action Group Exposure, 1991, opposes harsh and dangerous radiotherapy regimes. It presses for national standards in radiotherapy.

IDDT, the InDependent Diabetes Trust, 1994, criticises restrictions on the kinds of insulin offered to people with diabetes: they should be offered the full range, animal, human or analogue, with full information about treatment options.

APRIL, the Adverse Psychiatric Reactions Information Link, 1998, criticises the careless prescription and the perfunctory regulation of psychotropic drugs.

These patient activist groups are described in detail in my 2010 book. They can also be looked up on the internet. They, and the patients who approach them to recount their difficulties or to ask for help, see their work is needed as much as ever. Get rid of one harm and others may take its place.

The rise and fall of patient activist groups

Patient activist groups, like other social groups and movements, rise and fall with the tides of circumstances.

New developments in Medicine may call for new patient activist groups. In 2000, a new treatment for pelvic organ prolapse and urinary incontinence in women was introduced into clinical practice. Various sorts of mesh, usually of plastic, were used surgically to repair and support organs in the pelvis, like the uterus, vagina, or bladder, that had dropped or slipped out of their normal position. After the treatment, some women began to experience chronic pain and crippling conditions that could spoil their lives. They tried to tell their doctors. But they met with silence, denial, and sometimes contempt (Cumberlege, 2020). They formed patient groups to campaign against the treatment and to support their members. By 2020, there were at least 11 groups, including

Mashed up by Mesh, Sling the Mesh, and Action for Mesh Injured Patients. They gave evidence to the Cumberlege Review, an inquiry into the safety of medicines and medical devices. The Review exposed avoidable harm to patients; lack of information about possible side effects and so lack of informed consent; secrecy; undue variation in skill among surgeons; and an organisationally disjointed health service. Pharmaceutical companies, regulatory authorities, professional bodies, and policy-makers were held to have failed in their responsibilities (Cumberlege, 2020). From a political prospective, the Review is a study of patients' oppression and of their attempts to emancipate themselves.

Small voluntary patient activist groups may have their day of significance and influence, then their decline and fall. When all goes well, their desired standards become incorporated into mainstream professional and managerial practice. Then their origins in the work of activists and reformers is usually forgotten. Consumers for Ethics in Research (CERES) exemplifies this rise and fall. Founded in 1989, it challenged the ethical and scientific standards of clinical research. It closed in 2006 because its committee members thought that its main purpose had been achieved: the ethics of clinical research had improved, partly as a result of CERES members' work, writings, and contributions to official consultations. Less happily, committee members became over-burdened with telephone calls from patients asking for help; and the Department of Health, though sympathetic to the idea of a help-line, would not fund it. Members also discovered that researchers were giving out CERES leaflets to patient-participants in research instead of explaining their own research properly. So, acting from several reasons, CERES ceased. Its papers are archived in the Welcome Library in London.

Principles

Each patient activist group had its passionate members, and its allies and its enemies among doctors (chapter 4). Each group had its own aims, but common principles began to emerge.

People choose to act in some ways rather than in others, even if they can't explain exactly why. Patient activists noticed that they often tried to persuade doctors and other health professionals to offer more information to patients; to show them more respect; to offer them more choice; to allow them more support from friends and relatives; and to give them more control over what happened to them. These became patient activists' principles. They identified them – both discovered and created them – through observing what patients wanted; through their own intuitions and 'new knowledge'; and by keeping an eye on other emancipation movements and on medical ethics (Williamson, 1992).

Principles are guides to judgement and to action. Patient activists' principles were put into words by the late 1980s: support, information, control, choice, and shared decision-making (Williamson, 1992). (Control was later dropped, as too impractical.) By the mid-1990s, patient activists had added: equity (extending good care to all patients), access (to appointments, treatment, etc. for everyone); safety; representation; and redress (Williamson, 2010). These principles are embraced by most patients in the UK, since they are derived from patients themselves (Church, 2018). Even if most patients do not think about principles, they probably expect to find policies and practices that accord with them when they go into hospital or to their GPs' surgery. Just as women expect to vote and would protest if they were prevented from entering the polling station, patients may complain if they find information meagre, access to diagnosis or treatment long-delayed, shared decision-making not offered, and so on.

Of 1,444 complaints to York Teaching Hospital Trust in the year 2018/19, 413 were to do with clinical treatment; 231 with patientcare; 198 with communication; 177 with staff values and behaviours; 42 with privacy, dignity, and respect (York Teaching Hospital NHS Trust, 2019). These categories, set by the NHS Complaints Regulations, are broad. But they show where patients had found trouble in York Hospital.

The fundamental principle: autonomy

Thinking about the principles in the early 1900s, I saw that patients' autonomy could stand on its own as a fundamental value, underlying and unifying the principles. Act according to the principles and you support patients' autonomy: disregard them and you threaten it (Williamson, 1992). Other people must have had the same idea about the same time because the idea of autonomy for patients quickly caught on in social scientists' and in doctors' writings (Coulter, 2002; Gray, 2002). Patients' autonomy had been a value in medical ethics since at least 1977 (Beauchamp and Childress, 2009). But doctors had not always noticed that coercive practices breached that ethical value. (Not all have noticed, to this day.) It gave patients and doctors a value in common that could ultimately protect the autonomy of both (Williamson, 1992).

Autonomy can be defined in various ways, provided individuals' freedom to act without coercion by other people, and within the law, is stated or implied (Jenson and Mooney,1990). Various definitions and discussions of 'patient autonomy' from medical-ethical and medico-legal perspectives have been put forward. The discussion by the American medical ethicists, Tom L. Beauchamp and James F. Childress, is perhaps the most often cited. They say that patients' autonomy has to include or imply freedom from coercion, freedom of intention and choice, and ensuring that the patient understands these freedoms and the implications of the choices they make (Beauchamp and Childress, 2009, pp 103-117).

This is a definition by British patient activists:

Respect for patient autonomy means upholding patients' opportunities and abilities to control as far as possible the impact of illness or disability on their lives in ways that accord with their own moral and cultural values, their responsibilities to themselves, their families and their communities, and their interests as they define them. (Williamson, 2010, p 95).

Freedom from coercion is implied. Patients' opportunities and abilities to behave autonomously extend beyond making specific clinical decisions. Freedoms are not freedoms if they allow hidden coercions. Patients' interests 'as they define them' is a political point.

Both definitions mean that patients can choose to depend on their doctors' advice at any stage of their clinical care, if their temperaments or circumstances or strategic aims lead them to prefer that. If patients choose not to delegate their authority to their doctors, doctors should offer the patients enough information and enough time for discussion to help them make choices that are right for them. Patient and doctor can each contribute information and feelings to their discussion, perhaps coming up with ideas and courses of action that neither would have thought of on their own (Lown et al., 2009; Epstein and Street, 2011). To do that, doctors have to relinquish their stance of 'knowing best' what the patients' interests are (Chapter 1). This can be hard for doctors. They are pressed for time; directed by official protocols; perhaps lack skill or inclination. And, if Gerada's theory is right, it could put at risk their psychological defences (Chapter 1). But some manage it (Chapter 4).

Autonomy was not usually named as a principle in patient activist groups' early days. That vista was still too far away. But a recent patient activist group, Birthrights, founded in 2013, states that its purpose is to promote human rights in childbirth:

'All women are entitled to respectful maternity care that protects their fundamental rights to dignity, autonomy, privacy and equality' (Birthrights, 2019).

'Equality' here means 'equity' as between all women in childbirth, not equality with doctors and midwives (personal communication, Birthrights team, 2019). But words, like actions, can get new meanings.

The ethical requirement for doctors to respect patients' autonomy has become more compelling in recent years (Furness, 2003). 'Hospital scandals', where professional and ordinary social norms of behaviour break down, have perhaps helped doctors to focus on patients' autonomy and on how it can be interpreted and put into daily practice (Williamson, 2017). Doctors, however well-intentioned, do not always appreciate that even an apparently minor decision can have consequences that matter to that patient. In addition, autonomy is a political as well as an ethical value. Doctors and patients can find that confusing (Chapter 6).

Chapter 3

Patients specialise: roles and relationships

Challenging a dominant ideology takes time, patience, and multiple strategies.

Beverley Beech, patient activist, 2011, p 184.

Introduction

This chapter describes the structure of patients as a social group and the roles and relationships that have developed as the patient emancipation movement has gradually grown.

Three categories of patients

As patient activists gained new knowledge, experience, and expertise, they inevitably became different from other patients. They inadvertently created a new role, 'patient activists'. Their specialist knowledge contrasts with most patients' general knowledge. Activists are common in political groups, like environmental movements or anti–establishment demonstrations. They are essential in emancipation movements, where opposing the beliefs and policies of stronger, dominant social groups requires knowledge, determination, and persistence.

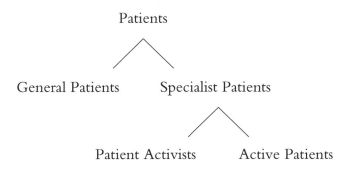

Patients

General Patients   Specialist Patients

Patient Activists   Active Patients

Figure 1. Categories of patients

Patient activists (also called patient advocates or patient representatives) work primarily to improve treatment and care for other patients. By the 1990s, a third new role had come into being: some patients had begun to see themselves as a new sort of patient, an active patient (Zakarian, 1996). Active patients (also called activist patients or e-patients) work primarily to improve their own treatment and care. In young social movements, both members and outsiders choose their own terms, creating confusion. (Confusion is a sign of hidden conflicts of goals, of views, and of interests.) I use 'patient activists' and 'active patients'. The three categories, general patients (sometimes called 'ordinary' patients, but few people are ordinary in the word's derogative meaning), patient activists, and active patients, overlap. Patients can move between them, as their circumstances, experiences, feelings, and knowledge change. The overall term for them is 'patients' just as cardiologists are 'doctors'. The rest of this chapter looks at these three categories.

General patients

Most patients have not set about gaining specialist knowledge, though when they become patients, some start to (Chapter 1). General patients often talk to friends about their experiences of hospitals or of GPs, especially while those experiences are fresh in their minds. But if the care was poor as they judge it, few take steps to improve it.

General patients' views and judgments about their care

Health professionals, managers, and social scientists tend to believe that general patients' views and judgments about their treatment and care differ from those of patient activists and active patients. They perhaps expect (or hope?) that general patients will be less critical. Yes and no. They have not acquired activists' theoretical knowledge or vocabulary. They don't have those feathers in their caps. But they still have caps. Their feelings about how they are treated are likely to be much the same as patient activists' and active patients'. After all, patient activists and active patients usually start as general patients. Various strands of evidence point to all patients having fundamental feelings and interests in common with each other. These feelings in common can be understood through 'the capabilities approach'.

The capabilities approach

1. The sociologist Vikki Entwistle and her colleagues searched 77 research reports into patients' experiences of how they were given

treatment and care and of how they felt about them. (They looked at 9,221 research reports to find those that matched their criteria for further examination. They searched only reports published in peer-reviewed journals, not in patient groups' journals.) They found that patients wanted themselves and their capabilities to be respected; to contribute to their own care; and to experience reciprocal relationships with their doctors and nurses. They valued being treated in such a way that they could 'feel, be and do' what they 'valued feeling, being and doing.' They especially valued staff's responsiveness to them as individual patients. Whether they were enabled or not enabled to feel, be and do what they valued, determined their feelings about their contacts with healthcare staff. It also affected their feelings about themselves and how well they could conduct their own lives. These feelings lasted long in their lives afterwards (Entwistle et al., 2012).

The authors interpreted their findings through 'the capabilities approach' put forward by the economist philosopher, Amartya Sen. Sen's capabilities approach links freedom and self-determination. In his book, *The Idea of Justice*, he says that one of the *valued aspects of living that we have reason to treasure* is *our freedom to determine the nature of our lives*. The freedom upholds our opportunities and our capabilities to *determine what we want, what we value and ultimately what we decide to choose* (Sen, 2009, pp 227,232).

Sen does not mention patients. But patientcare, especially in hospitals, necessarily restricts patients' freedoms to determine what they want and to make choices, to act autonomously. In normal social life, people's capacities and achievements are recognised through their jobs, their qualifications, their activities, their contributions to their families, friends and communities:

what they are and what they do. In hospital, most of these are stripped away. Supports for their sense of self can be threatened by their illness; by the lack of signs of their achievements and status; and by the many changes of staff and their transient relationships with them. Being ill in hospital can be like being cast overboard into a rough sea with only a flimsy plank to cling onto.

Stripping away patients' occupations, roles, and status in the world outside hospital also deprives staff of clues to patients' natures, to what they are like. Staff who in spite of this handicap, can show respect for patients and for their potential capabilities, can support patients' sense of selfhood, their sense of being. Staff who are dismissive or show impatience or contempt, can undermine that sense. Staff, especially nurses but also doctors, porters, and anyone who meets or talks to patients, vary so much that almost everything in patients' experiences depends on who is on duty that day or night and who is in charge of them. This, well-known to patients in hospital, has been confirmed by research (Goodrich and Cornwell, 2008).

2. The political theorist, Iris Marion Young, in her book *Justice and the Politics of Difference*, says that *all oppressed people suffer some inhibition of their ability to develop and exercise their capacities to express their needs, thoughts and feelings* (Young, 1990, p 40). (This fits with even articulate patients' self-reported failures to say all they intended in their consultations with doctors. Not all inhibitions depend on an individual doctor's dominance.) Young links freedom to self-determination and to justice. She defines injustice as the institutionalised conditions under which people cannot develop and exercise their capabilities as individual people, communicating and cooperating with other people (Young,

1990). These institutionalised conditions — the social structures and the attitudes and practices associated with them — are powerful in patientcare. ('Capacities', 'capabilities', and 'abilities' all have much the same meaning in the dictionary.) Young, like Sen, does not include patients in her list of disadvantaged social groups. Oppressed groups are not always seen as oppressed, until they emerge into the daylight of wide social knowledge.

A trivial but telling example of the pervasive institutional power to define things to suit health professionals: I recently pointed out to a dietician in York Hospital that the York Trust had a policy of asking patients how they wanted to be addressed, by first name or by title and surname, and using the mode they preferred. 'Oh', she said, 'I thought it was our preference'.

3. The patient in 1988 who wished her capabilities to be recognised said something important (Chapter 1). Her words, spoken before the capabilities approach was published, fit it exactly. *...I do not want to leave my personhood and capacities outside the door. How then can I use my resources to aid my recovery?*

4. The patients who were angry when their questions, informed by their knowledge acquired through their capacities to read, to remember, and to think, resulted in their doctors' sarcastic or reproachful answers (Chapter 1). Their sense of themselves and their capabilities was affronted.

5. Care that threatens or undermines patients' autonomy and sense of self-worth mildly or briefly is probably common. Patients may feel scorn or dislike for the health professionals who inflict it. But they can usually get over it fairly soon, especially if they can joke about it. Care that threatens or undermines patients' autonomy

severely or protractedly can make them feel extremely anxious and vulnerable. These effects can last well after the patient's recovery – indeed, for years. For an account of what this feels like, Mitzi Blennerhassett's book about her treatment for cancer, *Nothing Personal,* 2008, is painfully vivid. The cruelly inconsiderate and deceitful care she experienced has no generally accepted name. Perhaps few people want to recognise it or to think widespread. The British nurse, Paul Morrison, said this kind of care causes 'crushing vulnerability' to patients (Morrison, 1994). It is regularly evident in geriatric wards and care homes (Mandelstam, 2011). Reports on hospital scandals reveal it repeatedly.

6. The patient activists' definition of patients' autonomy in Chapter 2 (including freely chosen dependency) fits with the capabilities approach.

7. The American sociologist, Erving Goffman, noted in 1961 what he called 'non-person treatment'. ...*the patient is greeted with what passes as civility, and said farewell to in the same fashion, with everything in between going on as if the patient weren't there as a social person at all, but only as a possession someone has left behind.* (Goffman, 1968 p 298). In 2021, this may sound exaggerated; but Chapter 1 has current examples of patients thinking that some doctors do not see them 'as people'.

It's reasonable to conclude that general patients, patient activists, and active patients share, and have reasons to share, the same fundamental feelings about their care, even though general patients do not usually use the same words.

General patients as non-activists

Like non-activists in other emancipation movements, general patients are important in their own right, and not just because most patients are general patients. They are the constituents for whom patient activists work. Activists keep in touch with them. They talk to people in buses from bus stops near a hospital; sit with fellow patients in out-patients' departments where boredom and anxiety prompt conversation; wait companionably with them for investigations or treatments (hospital gowns remove the outward signs of social class); compare notes on doctors and procedures; form temporary bonds of affection with patients in the other beds; chat quietly in GPs' waiting rooms. In these encounters, patients exchange emotional support, information, and insights.

Patients sometimes get in touch with patient activist groups and describe their recent experiences and what they thought of them. Activist groups can draw out new ideas and new evidence (Robinson, 2004/5). They can publish patients' accounts of their care, good as well as bad, in their journals. Examples of good practice can encourage other patients to ask for them. If staff say that it is impossible and has never been done before, the patient then can cite an instance. If staff find the new practice good, they may adopt it. One swallow can make a summer.

General patients also form the test beds for activists' seedlings, their ideas and initiatives. If general patients expect to find in place standards that patient activists have proposed or promoted, they can help the new standards spread. This happens in other emancipatory movements (Mansbridge, 2001). Indeed, individual general patients are often seen by health professionals and managers as more 'authentic' or 'real' than patient activists. What a 'real' patient says seems to be uncontaminated by patient activism. It is also easy to dismiss as only one patient's opinion.

Research into patients' experiences and views can show how far patient activists' (or professionals' or managers') desired standards have been incorporated into routine treatment and care. Care can be poor because staff ignore accepted standards; or because it is oppressive; or because standards that should be in place are not (Williamson, 2000). All three sorts of poor care can occur together. Surveys of large samples of patients have repeatedly shown that high percentages of patients say they were not offered enough information nor took enough part in making decisions about their own treatment and care.

For shared decision-making, national surveys by Picker Institute Europe showed that, in 2006, 45% of hospital patients had not been involved in decisions about their care as much as they wanted to be (Richards and Coulter, 2007). In 2009, 50% of hospital patients had been involved as much as they wished. By 2017, this had risen to 56% (https://www.cgc.org.uk/publications/surveys/adult-inpatient-survey-2017/000) The question, 'Were you involved as much as you wanted to be in decisions about your care and treatment?' might mean different things to different patients, although Picker surveys are piloted. But there is an upward trend, although the percentage of patients who were not involved as much as they wanted to be is still high. That shows how little the accepted standards for shared decision-making are being followed. The wide gap between what patients want and what they are offered is striking in the 21st Century. (It can be used, like so much else, as evidence of patients' oppression.)

General patients and doctors

General patients can be critical of their doctors and wary of them. They can behave with more deference than they feel. They can show exaggerated gratitude. They can privately reject advice that they appear to comply with (Chapter 1). They can try to control the consultation instead of letting the doctor control it. Doctors used to think that patients who took into the consultation bits of paper with lists of points to raise were crazy (Gray, 2002). Those who took in computer printouts risked a frosty reception. The Royal College of General Practitioners has advised patients to make lists (RCGP, 1997). But change has come slowly, long after many patients have felt reprimanded for what they saw as helpful to the doctor as well to themselves. Doctors presumably saw patients' bits of paper as breaching the patient role. They sewed up the breach with sharp sarcastic needles.

Patients may think it prudent to adapt their remarks to save their doctor's feelings or to fend off their anger. People in a weaker position use common stratagems with those in a stronger position. Women get fed up with having their ideas ignored by men in meetings, then, a few minutes later, hearing them put forward by one of the men, unabashed, as his own (Beard, 2017). This has a name, 'mansplaining'. Without showing the anger they feel, women can use diffident instead of straightforward language. 'I'm just thinking out loud here' instead of 'I have an idea,' (McMahon, 2018). Patients who sense that a doctor does not respect them may resolve never to see him or her again.

Another hazard that patients (and patient activists) may meet is plagiarism, when doctors or nurses use their ideas without acknowledging them. Plagiarism is wrong in itself. It also hinders health professionals from appreciating the contributions patients can make to patientcare. Or patients' speeches or writings are not published in the first place. Or they are published but dissolved out of social or historical consciousness (Arksey, 1994). This is how women academics, poets, and painters have often fared in the past (Aisenberg and Harrington,1988). So do women doctors now (Dacre, 2019). None of this is different from the trials that men and male doctors may experience. It is just probably more common.

General patients politically

Although so important in their own right, individual general patients are politically weak when they are appointed to high level official working parties or committees. They can describe their own experiences in enthralling detail. But they cannot speak for (represent) the interests of other patients (Williamson, 2007). They seldom know what those interests are. Even if they do know, they are unlikely to have to hand arguments and evidence that would support what they say. Arguing with professionals or managers requires more than strong feelings: it also requires knowledge and skill (Martin and White, 2003). General patients also lack the support of colleagues. That support helps patient activists stand up to and counter the more powerful voices of the other members of the group or committee (Oliver et al., 2001).

Health professionals and managers are sometimes surprised that putting one or two general patients onto a committee seldom works well. But it is predictable. Indeed, it is normal: expertise as well as experience is necessary for those taking part in high level discussions and decisions in any sphere of life. General patients are at their best on local professional-patient committees discussing the details of the care that they have recently experienced. What was it like to be in Ward 26 for a week last November? have a baby? have a skin biopsy? Only they know that.

When patients and clinicians are together in local working groups, neither should be nor have recently been in clinical relationships with each other. Both could be embarrassed or inhibited. This is also so for clinicians and patient activists in national working parties and committees (Williamson, 1997). But it is less likely to happen there.

Patient activists

These are patients or former patients who aim to represent, in the sense of speak for, the interests of other patients. They are not conduits for patients' views though they try to give voice to their interests. This distinction rests on the difference between personal experience and abstract knowledge. The first is valid for patients who put into words their personal experiences. The second takes into account the experiences and views of many patients, abstracted into coherent positions, statements or questions. It also takes into account threats to patients' interests that general patients may be unaware of because of doctors' and institutions' secrecy (Alford, 1975). Patient activists don't know as much as they would like to about doctors' hidden assumptions and practices. But they are likely to know more than general patients. Secrecy, whether deliberate or accidental, is a powerful political way of nipping opposition in the bud before it can open into a flower that attracts attention.

Health professionals and managers, and sometimes patients, can find differences between kinds of patients confusing. This is because the patient emancipation movement has not yet fully explained itself either to itself or to others. Besides, some patient activists are more experienced and expert than others. Health professionals and managers can find it difficult to judge the validity of what they say and how far it can be generalised. It is easier to charge activists with being 'unrepresentative' (Hogg, 2009). Or to see them as 'self-selected' or having 'bees in their bonnets'. Or to declare that activists are not 'real' patients (Hogg, 2009; Williamson, 2018).

Sneering at people who work to emancipate oppressed groups is well known to the women's and the civil rights movements. Women are called 'bra-burners' or 'man-haters', black people, the n-word. Most charges against patient activists are silly. But the 'not real patients' charge is worth examining.

Patient activists are often told that they are too knowledgeable and too articulate to be 'real' patients. They are damned with patronising praise. Doctors who say patient activists are not 'real' patients forget that they themselves can be doctoring one day in remote rural Lincolnshire, debating in a national committee in central metropolitan London, the next. Patient activists, when they are patients in clinical relationships, feel the same anxieties, doubts, hopes, and fears as other patients. When they are patient activists, they draw on different knowledge, feelings, social skills. Both patient activists and doctors are 'real'. Denying that to activists is a subtle, perhaps unconscious, way of dismissing what they say. Conversely, when doctors can accept patient activists for what they are, the doctors can throw off the inhibitions and anxieties they feel in clinical relationships. They can discuss sensitive matters freely. Perhaps they can enjoy feelings of equality with their fellow committee members. Perhaps they can experience the relationships of mutual trust and equality that patient activists hope all patients and doctors will one day achieve (Hogg, 1999).

Like women who are not feminists and black, Asian and minority ethnic people who are not civil rights activists or anti-racist campaigners, general patients benefit from activists' work. They may be unaware of that. Do parents in the UK with a sick young child or baby in hospital with whom they can stay as long as they like (for 24 hours, 7 days a week) know that it took a patient activist group, the National Association for the Welfare of Children in Hospital (NAWCH) more than 30 years of unremitting effort to secure that freedom for them? Even though it had been known since the 1960s that children in hospital needed their parents' protection and support? (Belson, 2004; Williamson, 1992). Doctors and nurses may also be unaware of the history of their current policies and practices. So each new proposal from patients or patient activists can seem solitary and startling, rather than part of normal social and political processes.

As other emancipation movements find, some people who might be affected by oppression are hostile to activists. That does not prevent them benefitting from activists' work.

Active patients

Patients who want to take charge of the treatments for their diseases call themselves active or activist patients (Zakarian,1996). They carry out researches and communicate with other patients on the internet (Riggare, 2018). They research what's known about their disease and its treatments (Schneider, 2005). They choose which treatment they should have, and, if refused, go to a different doctor or hospital. Here I draw largely on three active patients' accounts of what they did. Beverly Zakarian had ovarian cancer stage III, usually fatal; Stephen Schneider, mantle cell lymphoma stage IV, usually fatal; Sara Riggare, Parkinson's disease, disabling and life-shortening. Many people become active patients to some degree. These three show it in its purest form.

Active patients spend their time and energy only on diseases that are likely to be fatal or disabling. They think that many doctors, however well-intentioned and expert, have too little time to search for all the treatments that might help patients as seriously ill as they are (Schneider, 2005; Riggare, 2018). They want treatments tailored to their individual clinical situations. They want to take responsibility for the timing as well as for the nature of their treatments. Every aspect of their treatment is important to them (Riggare, 2018). It is they, the patients, who have the greatest stake in their own health; the closest familiarity with their body's physical and psychological states; and its reactions to earlier episodes of healthcare. It is they who have the ultimate moral authority for how they conduct their lives. *No one has more to gain. No one cares more about the outcome* (Zakarian, 1996, p 19).

Active patients try to find doctors who will be highly competent clinically; will accept their values and purposes; will respect their knowledge, academic, professional, occupational, experiential or other; and will be willing to work collaboratively with them. Respect for each other's capabilities is crucial. Mutual respect and liking are desirable in any therapeutic relationship. They are essential for collaborative therapeutic working because only the doctor (or sometimes the nurse) can prescribe treatment. When their doctors and nurses help them as only they can, with goodwill, clinical knowledge, experience and skill, active patients are extremely grateful; they know that generosity is needed to care for patients as exacting as they (Schneider, 2005).

Through their researches and communications with other patients on the internet, active patients may come across treatments that their doctor might not know about or offer, yet that might be crucial for their survival (Riggare, 2018). Active patients' ability to get in touch through the internet with specialists and patients, however distant geographically, lets them give and take information. They can tell their doctors of their discoveries. They can form virtual patient groups, giving each other information, tips for handling distressing treatments or their side effects, and emotional support. This support from virtual groups can help active patients be confident and articulate, just as actual patient groups do for their members. They may favour treatments that some doctors think are ineffective or harmful. That can happen in actual patient groups. It can happen between different doctors. Uncertainty is inherent in Medicine.

Active patients can help improve the quality and safety of care. According to their backgrounds and to the knowledge they acquire in their researches, they can sometimes detect clinical, psychosocial or ethical flaws in the clinical protocols and routine procedures they observe or experience. Stephen Schneider was a climate scientist. With his knowledge of currents of air, he noticed that the doors from the hospital corridor, the vestibule and the inner door to the microbiologically clean room he was in, were sometimes all left open at the same time, allowing contaminated air to get into his room. Again, with his statistical expertise, he calculated that too few blood samples were being taken from patients like him to show accurately when healthy white blood cells fell to their lowest level. That number was necessary to decide when to give the next lot of chemotherapy (Schneider, 2005). He pointed out these and other flaws to his doctors and nurses, to protect himself and other patients. Sometimes staff responded with indifference or with defensiveness. They blamed hospitals' hierarchical systems that inhibited lower status staff from criticising higher status staff. But sometimes they made changes (Schneider, 2005). He titled his book *The Patient from Hell,* though he added the soothing subtitle, *How I Worked with My Doctors to Get the Best of Modern Medicine and How You Can Too.* He survived his cancer, though, sadly, he died of a heart attack on an airplane in 2010, aged 65.

Active patients behave contrary to Parson's model and its lingering influences (Chapter 1), except for their desire to get well or to stop getting worse. Like patient activists, they work in an emancipatory direction, drawing intuitively or deliberately on the principles that support their own and other patients' autonomy. These principles can be seen from the words in active patients' accounts. *Information; choice* (of doctor and team, of hospital, as well as of treatment); *shared decision-making; respect* (from doctors and all staff)*; support* (from family, friends, healthcare staff, and sometimes from paid professional advocates); *access* (to a good hospital, doctors; method of paying for their diagnosis, treatment and care); and *safety*. Patients' safety means ensuring that no avoidable harm comes to them. Safety also means that they are told about the risks and benefits of various possible treatments. Then they can balance the nature and frequency of the potential risks against the hoped-for benefits (Zakarian, 1996; Williamson, 2010). They can always choose to have no treatment, or no further treatment; but the choice must be theirs. *Equity* looks as if it would not fit into this emancipatory picture, because well-informed, determined patients, with enough money or insurance to pay for their treatment and care, if necessary, could be expected to be more effective than ill-informed, helpless or poor ones. But equity can mean levelling up, by giving extra clinical, social and emotional support to patients who need it. Some doctors and managers interpret equity as levelling down so that no patients benefit. That is a strongly repressive view (Williamson, 2007b).

Some patients have long been quietly active patients. They have learnt to search for information and to have the courage to speak up to their doctors (Hammond, 2015). That to speak up to your doctor or to show how much you know takes courage, tells us how effectively social structures have enforced repressive views of how doctors and patients should behave. Again, dominance is dominant because people accept it. As one patient, herself a doctor, said 'You have to be educated but not seem crazy' (personal communication, 2018).

Quietly active patients comply with the medical advice and institutional policies that they think good or unimportant. Then they can more easily decline procedures or medications they don't want. Or they can ask for others they do want. (Saving one's credibility by not opposing too much, too often, is a political strategy used by power-low people, though not only by them – it is part of many negotiations.) They know that being a 'good' patient, compliant, cooperative, cheerful, will stand them in good stead, if differences of opinion between them and their doctors, midwives or nurses arise. Smiling and seeming cheerful, as well as not talking too much, is a precaution that women take with men, and black, Asian and minority ethnic people with white people. Subordinate non-human primates also signal submission to the more powerful members of their social group (Wilson, 1975).

As part of their scrutiny of care, active patients can try to find out whether any managerial or clinical policies or protocols restrict the treatments and care they could be offered. Hospitals and general practices are not always frank about restrictive policies; but their consequences for patients can be serious (Williamson, 2005). If patients discover that restrictions are in place, they can sometimes argue against them or move to another hospital. Or they might start a new patient activist group to oppose them. Even being only occasionally an active patient demands energy as well as persistence. Energy is exactly what illness or treatment can impair. The paradox that health and strength are needed to oppose oppression that affects the ill and weak comes up again (Chapter 1).

The ideology of the patients' emancipation movement

A social group's ideology is a set of ideas to guide its members' actions and explain them to the outside world. It has to be in tune with its members' feelings and intuitions and it must have theoretical justifications. *Without intellectual and theoretical underpinnings, no movement can succeed…* (Heilbrun, 1989, p. 20). A new group's or social movement's ideology may take time to be developed and put into words by its members, even after they have reached the once-distant vista. But members must not leave the analysis and creative synthesis of their ideas, values, and beliefs too long. If they do, the group's ideas and purposes may fall by the wayside. Or they may be appropriated and changed by other social groups. No-one knows what 'too long' is or how to allow for splits or schisms among the members. Patient activism's emancipatory ideology is still largely intuitive. But it is clear to some patients, patient activists, active patients and doctors.

Conclusion

Patient activists, working to free patients from harmful practices and policies, and active patients, working to free themselves, have used and developed their capabilities. They now need to find how to raise patients' status and political power (Chapter 6). Patients' alliances with doctors can help towards this (next chapter).

Chapter 4

Doctors respond

Since the physician-patient interaction requires the participation of two persons, the perspectives of both must be integrated into any theoretical construct.

Allan Brett, physician, and Laurence McCullough, researcher, 1986, p 1349.

Introduction

Emancipation movements come into being when members of a weaker or subordinate social group ask members of a stronger or dominant social group to change some of their ways and the stronger group refuses. Without that resistance, there would be no emancipation movement. But paradoxically, emancipation movements can be helped by members of dominant social groups. Some of their members can ally themselves with members of the subordinate group. They can work with them or accept their views. This chapter looks at doctors who have allied themselves with patients, at least to some extent, and so have helped the emancipation of patients. (Alliances began before emancipation was thought of, so it was not doctors' purpose then and probably is seldom consciously so now.) But first, this chapter looks briefly at doctors' resistance.

Resistance

At its height of doctors' power, Medicine's 'golden age' from the 1940s to the 1960s, doctors took it for granted that they knew what their patients' interests were. They gave advice and treatment in that paternalistic belief (Freidson, 2001). Many patients also believed that their doctors acted in their interests. (Parson's scheme, 1951, assumed it.) When patients' confidence in their doctors' actions began to break down and they began to criticise the quality of medical care, many doctors reacted with indifference, scepticism, or anger (Blumenthal, 1996). Dr Blumenthal was a physician in Massachusetts but doctors' reactions were the same in the UK. 'Patients don't understand' was a common cry. Doctors' anger suggests that they felt the same threats to their personhoods and their capabilities that patients feel when they think their doctors do not respect them.

Doctors' resistance to what patients, including active patients, say is common (Riggare, 2018). Resistance seems to be a cultural response in the medical profession. Dame Deidre Hine, former Chief Medical Officer for Wales, said that doctors were unwilling to accept changes that they saw as damaging the interests of their profession or its specialties, if the changes involved 'some loss of influence, area of practice, or status' (Hine, 2007, p 60). That is, some loss of power. In addition, doctors are trained to think of the medical and the lay worlds as separate and to exclude the lay world (Sinclair, 1997). They also learn to think of themselves as different from patients (Chapter 1). Such thorough and intensive socialisation into their profession is likely to make doctors resist ideas and requests coming from lay people. If they come from a doctor, they are more likely to be accepted. Once, when I was a non-voting member of the council of the Royal Council of General Practitioners, something controversial came up. I was about to speak, when a doctor, sitting next to me, scribbled on a slip of paper, 'leave this to me'. I did; and she successfully said what I would have said. Resistance is conditional.

Allies

A minority of doctors show little resistance to patients' ideas, provided patients justify them by argument or evidence. These doctors seem to be unusually sensitive to patients' views and interests. Politically, they align some of their own interests with those of patients. They sometimes support patients' interests when they conflict with those of mainstream Medicine. They seem willing to cede some of their power to patients. They sometimes come up with patient-aligned ideas of their own.

From the earliest days of patient activism in the 1960s, patient activists recognised these doctors as allies. Their power to get things done through their positions in their hospitals, GP practices or membership of other organisations; their acceptability to their medical colleagues; their access to policy makers at every level of the NHS; their high status beyond their profession; and their advice and friendship benefit patient activists and patients. Reciprocally, the doctors get stimulus, new ideas and perspectives, approval and support from their allies. Approval and support can be welcome because these doctors sometimes meet hostility from other doctors. Heroes to patients and patient activists, to other doctors, they can be traitors.

Patient activists called doctors who supported patients' interests against mainstream Medicine's views and interests 'good professionals' (Williamson, 1992). (The comparable term in the women's movement is 'men of goodwill', Tong, 1997). A better term than 'good professional' is 'patient-aligned' because that makes a trio with 'doctor-aligned' and 'manager-aligned'. Doctors' choices are political. But that is not always clear to doctors because they tend to pay little attention to healthcare politics (Chapter 6). The women's movement's aphorism 'the personal is political' fits these alignments: what feels personal has political implications, and what is political can be felt personally.

Doctors' patient-alignment can be seen both in doctor-patient relationships and at policy level. At the doctor-patient level, it has been called 'allies versus non-allies' for doctors who believed in repetitive strain injury and those who did not (Arksey, 1994) and 'progressive versus traditionalist' for doctors who treated cancer patients as individuals versus those who used 'a one size fits all' protocol (Schneider, 2005). The idea comes into some patients' descriptions of their experiences with doctors, even though they seldom give it a name.

At the policy level of doctors debating in the councils of the medical royal colleges or the General Medical Council, or of writing articles, terms overlap with those for individual doctor-patient relationships. They include 'progressive-conservative' for doctors who support making the General Medical Council more sympathetic to the public's (patients' and lay people's) expectations versus those who resist that (Irvine, 2017); 'radical-conservative' for those who challenge the status quo in patientcare versus those who do not (Williamson, 2010); and 'patient friendly –

patient non-friendly' as general terms (Patricia Wilkie, personal communication, 2018). Do these different terms mean the same thing? Are they synonyms? Or are they a set of closely related variables? Do doctors' personal practices and the positions they take at policy level coincide? Probably they are consistent for each doctor. But we can't be sure without evidence from research.

Using the terms patient-aligned versus patient non-aligned, we can envisage a range of positions between strongly patient-aligned and weakly patient-aligned or non-patient aligned. Experienced patient activists can spot patient-aligned doctors and patient non-aligned doctors from their published writings or public pronouncements. But the signs can be subtle. As in all political matters, what is not said may be as important as what is.

Alignments, moreover, can shift according to the topics and the controversial issues being considered. Healthcare professionals' and managers' ability to change their usual positions on controversial issues enables changes to policies and practices to be made (Alford, 1975). This is so in ordinary life, too. How we see our interests can be more important than which social group we belong to.

Patient-aligned doctors speak

In 2008, I interviewed five patient-aligned doctors to ask them if they could say what had made them that. (I used the term 'radical' but they understood what I meant.) The sample was tiny. But I knew their alignments from working closely with them on national committees. That was more important than total objectivity, even supposing that were possible. It did not affect how I worded the questions; but it made for pleasant and candid interviews. Two anaesthetists, a GP, an oncologist, and a pathologist kindly agreed to be interviewed. With their permission, I give their names and their specialties.

They had all been medical students when they had witnessed something they particularly remembered. Each had seen an incident of doctors' behaviour towards a patient that had struck them as wrong. But it had not disturbed their fellow students.

Ann Johnson was in a cancer unit where care seemed 'inhumane', not fitting for human beings. But it could not be altered. She had wondered if 'inhumanity was an aspect of medicine?' (1953).

Catti Moss knew that a patient had died on the operating table because though doctors had read his notes, they had not talked to him and so had not known he had heart disease. She also saw an elderly woman resuscitated only because she had lied about her age. She had pretended to be 63 so she that could continue working. She was 75, above the cut-off age for resuscitation in that hospital. Catti Moss had decided that 'Medicine was not all it was cracked up to be' (1975).

Andrew Smith saw a patient who had had a stroke wheeled into a lecture theatre and examined for abnormal neurological signs in front of 140 students. He had wondered what the patient thought (1983).

Helen William's mother had untreatable cancer. Her doctors had concealed her imminent death from her. Helen Williams had seen that there were valid perspectives other than those of Medicine (1974).

The fifth respondent could not recall any specific incident.

These crucial experiences took place before these doctors were fully socialised into the medical profession. That is, before they had accepted its assumptions, values, attitudes towards patients, and psychological defence mechanisms (Chapter 1). They seem instead to have retained lay sensitivities, feelings and thoughts. They reacted to these incidents with surprise or shock, as many lay people would. These medical students had not yet developed 'wilful blindness', the capacity not to see certain painful aspects of reality (Heffernan, 2011). We all are blind to some things but not to others. That defends us from being overwhelmed and incapacitated by 'tears for the nature of things and hearts touched by human transience' (Virgil, *Aeneid*, Book 1).

These medical students' experiences of disillusioned enlightenment or damascene moments were like those that can strike future patient activists when they first meet aspects of patientcare that they believe harm themselves or patients like them (Chapter 2). Like the patient activists, the doctors seem to have been permanently changed. But they remained doctors. Indeed, they became highly respected. Dr Johnson took up research as well as clinical oncology, finally returning to the same hospital whose cancer unit she had deplored. As a consultant she was able to change it into a place so welcoming and comfortable that long after their treatment, patients returned to it for pleasure. Dr Moss was elected a member of the Royal College of General Practitioners' council. She was well-known for her radical (i.e. patient-aligned) views and was immensely helpful to its patient liaison group. Later, she was appointed an honorary associate clinical professor of medical education. Dr Smith wrote discussion papers as well as research papers and became a professor of anaesthetics. He was invaluable to the working group described later in this chapter. Dr Williams became the Registrar of the Royal College of Pathologists. She founded its patient liaison group and was crucial to its early success. That these doctors could combine patient-alignment with eminence in their own medical fields should give courage to other doctors.

A few patient-aligned doctors have written about their conversions and experiences. Dr Wendy Savage and Sir Donald Irvine are examples. Both offered their patients more information, more choice and more responsibility than was usual at the time. Both experienced the hostility that patient-alignment can arouse. Dr Savage was supported through dire difficulties by the maternity care patient activist groups. the Association for Improvements in the Maternity Service, AIMS, and the National Childbirth Trust, NCT. Their members and local people marched through streets near her hospital in London in June 1985 in protest at her suspension from her post. After a public inquiry, she was reinstated (Savage, 1986). She was elected to the General Medical Council, years later, from 1989-2005. One of Sir Donald Irvine's reforms is recounted later in this chapter. Power, professional culture, and whose views shall prevail, are intensely important in healthcare, even apart from their relevance to patients' emancipation.

We don't know how many doctors are strongly patient-aligned. But they probably have an influence beyond their numbers. They are directly or indirectly helpful to patients' emancipation. Doctors' work for standards of care, so important to patients as well as to doctors, shows this.

Doctors and standards of medical care and practice

Doctors have drawn up standards for giving medical care, probably ever since medical work began. Standards reflect values, beliefs, perspectives, and interests. They are always potentially controversial. In *Middlemarch* by George Eliot we see disagreements between the hero, the newcomer Dr Lydgate, and the older, longer established doctors in the town. Their conflicts and ill-feelings over standards are intractable (Eliot, 1871-2). Doctors now draw up sets of standards, nationally in the medical royal colleges and specialty associations, and locally in clinical commissioning groups, clinical departments in hospitals and GPs' surgeries. When in the 1960s patient activist groups began to oppose some of those standards, and did so successfully, the medical profession began to change. Since then, many new ideas from Medicine itself and from other social groups as well as from patient activists contributed to change and continue to contribute.

* Some patient groups drew up and published their own sets of standards, just as some professional organisations did. So what patients, via those patient groups, wanted patientcare to be like began to be discernible (Chapter 2).

* Community Health Councils (CHCs), set up by the government in 1974 to represent (speak for) patients' and the community's interests to NHS management, focussed attention on those interests (Klein and Lewis, 1976). CHCs were composed of representatives from local patient groups and of representatives of the local authority. Members could compare patients' experiences and interests from different care groups. They could build up expertise in speaking for the interests of patients in general as well

as for those in specific categories, like those needing geriatric care or blood transfusions.

CHC members learnt to be cogent critics of under-provision of services and of low standards of care. The government abolished CHCs in 2003. Some doctors and some managers had complained about them; their performances had varied; and they had begun to criticise the government itself (Gerrard, 2006). Abolition removed lay people's close surveillance of local hospital wards. It did away with their relationships with local hospital doctors and managers. CHCs were also an ideal training ground for patient activists and for ambitious NHS managers. CHCs' loss set back patient activism. Local doctors and managers also lost early warnings about unsatisfactory standards. Every government 'patient and public involvement' project since has been less effective (and more expensive) than CHCs (Hogg, 2009).

Government schemes to promote patients' interests have been fragile. The medical profession has done better.

* Some doctors in the US saw that high standards for patientcare came from responding to patients' preferences and values, especially to individual patients in clinical consultations. Doctors should marry their perspectives to those of patients (Blumenthal, 1996). In the UK, doctors began to invite members of patient groups to join them in setting standards. Setting those standards implicitly sets standards for how doctors should practice. This double effect probably contributes to some doctors' opposition to new patient-aligned standards.

* The medical royal colleges began in 1983 to form national patient liaison groups. These are working groups of a small

numbers (usually 5-10) of their members and a roughly equal number of patient group members or patient activists or other lay people. Patient liaison groups enable their medical and lay members to discuss problems and standards of care freely. Sensitive and controversial issues can be explored without embarrassment because none of the members know anything about the clinical records or clinical practices of anyone else (Williamson, 1998).

The first medical royal college to start a patient liaison group was the Royal College of General Practitioners (Williamson, 1993). By 2017, most of the 22 medical royal colleges and faculties had some form of patient or lay group (Wikipedia, 2019). The non-medical members' backgrounds vary and not all are suited to the task of 'critical friend' (Bath et al., 2017). Sometimes colleges appoint lay people rather than patient activists. Lay people's contributions, though valuable in their own right, lack patient activists' specialised knowledge, insights and potential criticisms. Choosing members can be a dilemma for the colleges, one that they sometimes approach timidly.

Other doctor-patient working groups include patient participation groups in general practice, clinical audit groups, research groups designing research protocols, and research ethics groups.

★ Some of the standards that patients and activists want to see adopted fit with Medicine's ethical standards and values. An ethical value in common is autonomy for patients, although how it is defined, interpreted, and put into practice, varies (Chapters 2 and 6).

It's hard to say exactly what these doctor-patient groups have contributed to patientcare; to the profession of Medicine; and to the emancipation of patients. Much has depended on the how far the doctor members have been patient-aligned. But opposition from patient non-aligned doctors is always a hazard, both within the groups and from outside them. Sometimes opposition is open. Sometimes it waits to be provoked. Then it may jump out on patient-aligned doctors; or on their work with other doctors; or on their work with patient activists.

Two publications illustrate doctors' patient-alignment: *Good Medical Practice,* 1995, and *Anaesthesia explained,* 2003. (General Medical Council, 1995; Royal College of Anaesthetists and Association of Anaesthetists of Great Britain and Ireland, 2003). They also illustrate some of the difficulties of the work. Yet difficulties are bound to arise, if patients' interests are being fully considered (Parroy et al., 2003).

Good Medical Practice, 1995

The General Medical Council (GMC) regulates the medical profession in the UK (GMC, 2013). Its president from 1995–2002 was Dr Donald Irvine (later Sir Donald Irvine). When he was elected president of the GMC, Medicine's standing with the public was low because it seemed to favour doctors' interests conspicuously over patients' interests. Irvine set out to lead change within the profession. He and colleagues decided to produce a new statement about the profession's values and standards, duties, and responsibilities. A working party, chaired by him, produced a booklet to guide doctors' performance, *Good Medical Practice* (GMC, 1995). It included several patient activist principles: Information *you must give the information [patients] ask for or need about their condition, its treatment and prognosis* p 4; Shared decision-making *you must respect the rights of patients to be fully involved in decisions about their care* p 4 ; Respect *you must treat patients politely and considerately, listen to [them] and respect their views* p 4; Safety *you must recognise the limits of your professional competence, and refer the patient to another practitioner, when indicated* p 2. These were put forward as professional principles, not as patient principles. (The words 'patient autonomy' were not in the text; the idea had not become common among UK doctors by 1995, though the principles supported it, Chapter 2.)

Irvine's working party included no patient activists. Its members were three members of the GMC council, Professor Charles George, Professor Wendy Savage, Dr Michael O'Donnell and two non-members, Dr John Harvard, a former secretary of the British Medical Association, and Ian Kennedy QC a medical ethicist who had written *The Unmasking of Medicine,* a critique of Medicine. Of these five, three could be said to be patient-aligned, with Sir Donald Irvine as a fourth (Kennedy, 1981; Savage, 1986; O'Donnell, Illman, 2019).

Irvine had consulted patient organisations, like the Patients Association. He had long conversations with individual activists, inviting them to the GMC headquarters in Hallam Street, London. So patients and patient activists had contributed indirectly to *Good Medical Practice.* Irvine's stance at the GMC and in the patient-alignment of *Good Medical Practice* were so evident that doctors hostile to him accused him of 'going native with patients' (recounted in a eulogy at his funeral, 3 December 2018).

Good Medical Practice is updated every few years and a copy of each new edition is sent to every doctor registered with the GMC. It is sent free to anyone else who asks for it. Some patient activists use it as a handbook for judging the quality of patientcare and medical practice. They want to see copies of it in every hospital ward and in every GPs' surgery (Patricia Wilkie, personal communication, 2018). They can use the broad principles for criticising current standards. Or they can put forward new standards that fit into the principles. Patients could use it to support their requests in hospitals or in GPs' surgeries, though probably few know that.

The GMC expects doctors to comply with the principles in *Good Medical Practice*. But whereas it says that they must comply with some standards under all circumstances, it only says that they should comply with others, if possible (GMC, 2013). Even official expectations, however authoritative and reasonable, do not necessarily translate into what doctors do. Information and shared decision-making, in particular, are still sometimes scant or non-existent. Some doctors say they do not always practice them. They haven't enough time to offer information to patients or to guide them through shared decision-making (Ives et al., 2018). Or they believe that patients will lose confidence in the doctor (Chapter 1). Or they say that patients will dither and so delay effective treatment (Kay, 2017). It is a mark of medical power that doctors can publically say that they disregard standards in *Good Medical Practice* and yet evoke no response from the GMC. Nevertheless, *Good Medical Practice* is a major advance for patient emancipation through its patient-aligned principles and standards.

Revisions of *Good Medical Practice* have strengthened its patient-aligned messages. The latest edition, 2013, says *The investigation or treatment you provide or arrange must be based on the assessment you and your patient make of their needs and priorities* ... p 19. This takes shared decision-making almost for granted.

Good Medical Practice was and is a remarkable support to patients' emancipation, though that was not, as far as I know, its authors' intention. For doctors and patients alike, 1995 was an important year.

Anaesthesia explained, 2003

The medical royal colleges are responsible for setting detailed standards for patientcare in their specialities, standards consistent with the broad standards in *Good Medical Practice*. When the patient liaison group of the Royal College of Anaesthetists was formed in 1998, its members put standards for information for patients high on its agenda. They wrote a paper for the college's council saying what written information for patients should cover. Council members rejected it unanimously. The patient liaison group kept calm and cheerful and bided its time. This is an intuitive strategy that disadvantaged social groups fall back on when protest could be dangerous. Many black people in the southern states of US used it after the emancipation of slaves in 1863. *The Help* describes the violence black people could meet from white people, if they protested. The danger for the patient liaison group was its demise through being disbanded. But sure enough, two years later, the college started an ambitious project, proposed by one of its anaesthetist members, to set national standards for information for patients. It took another two years to complete. Hospitals still give its leaflets to patients today.

Anaesthesia is a specialty that by its nature allows no casual deviations from high clinical standards. If anaesthetists or patients mess about, death or paralysis can follow immediately. Anaesthetists can compensate for this lack of freedom for themselves and their patients by scrupulous attention to seeking consent or refusal to every course of action they propose; by offering patients as many choices of those actions as they can; by giving explanations of the reasons for specific courses of action and of the benefits and risks attached to them, with shared decision-making to the extent each patient wants it This makes writing information for patients exacting, for it is especially important to get the style and tone right – if the writers can agree on what those are.

Led by the council member who proposed the project, Dr Alastair Lack, a team of six anaesthetists and a team of six patient activists worked together. The anaesthetists were: Dr Alastair Lack, chair, Dr Anna-Maria Rollin, Dr Andrew Smith, Dr Gavin Thoms, and Dr Lucy White. The patient activists were: Mrs Mitzi Blennerhassett, Mr Roger Goss, Mrs Ann Seymour, Mrs Madeleine Wang, Dr Patricia Wilkie, and Dr Charlotte Williamson. (The authors' names were listed in the report on the project, Lack et al., 2003, but not in the booklet or the leaflets. Nowadays, they should be, for accountability.) They wrote the core booklet *Anaesthesia explained* and a shorter matching leaflet *You and your anaesthetic*. They oversaw the creation of ten briefer leaflets, each on a specialist area of anaesthetics – paediatric anaesthesia, spinal anaesthesia, cardiovascular anaesthesia, and so on. These were written by groups of anaesthetists, patients, patient activists and relevant staff in hospitals across the country. For the leaflets, the anaesthetists were always in a minority and the patients always had had experience of the procedures being written about. (Sometimes patients are regarded as all the same, whatever their experience or its lack.) The leaflet writers were guided and the leaflets checked for compatibility with the core booklet by Dr Rollin. Mrs Sue Parroy, a former physiotherapist, was the project manager. She gave administrative and emotional support to its members, as well as contributing insights of her own.

Altogether, 165 people were involved, some briefly, others for months (Lack et al., 2003).

For *Anaesthesia explained,* the patient activists were experienced and strongly patient-aligned. All had been chairs or members of their local Community Health Councils and of local or national patient groups. They checked proposals, paragraphs, and sentences against patient activist principles and their own 'new knowledge'. Did the texts of drafts support ample information, shared decision-making, support, safety, respect, and so on? In addition, they knew from their own and other patients' experiences what were doctors' common 'patient put-downs' − baby talk, reluctance to give clinical information, lack of introductions, and so on (Chapter 1). They knew about Medicine's occasional breaches of ethics or of humanity. They didn't know much about anaesthesia to begin with. They learnt as they went along. But their perspectives remained different from those of their anaesthetist colleagues.

The anaesthetists' alignments varied. One was strongly patient-aligned, the others to different degrees according to the issues being discussed. They drew mostly on their professional experiences, clinical knowledge, and responses to the patient activists' ideas. They, too, learnt as they went along, and worked hard to accommodate the patient activists' views about the contents and wording of the publications.

Nevertheless, the work was surprisingly stressful for both the anaesthetists and the patient activists. Reasons for stress that might apply to other working or writing parties include:

1. Feelings run deep when the quality of patientcare is discussed. We all fear that we will not receive good treatment and care when we need them, as well as fearing disease and disablement.

2. Discussions about the quality of and standards of care, what to write down, what advice to offer patients, and other controversial topics, take time. Ideas that people reject today, they may accept tomorrow. Time passes, the sky doesn't fall down, colleagues seem comfortable with the draft texts. But this working group had little time for slow maturation.

3. Patient-alignment and patient non-alignment are political positions. Political positions easily stir up ill-feeling, as we saw with Brexiteers versus Remainers. These alignments were seldom recognised in the early 2000s so members did not put them into words during the project.

4. The anaesthetists were more powerful than the patient activists within their college and within wider society. But theirs were the assumptions and views that the patient activists challenged. This can be stressful for the more powerful group's members, forced to look at their own and their colleagues' accustomed beliefs and ways of working. It can be stressful for the weaker group's

members who must judge how far to press their demands for changes and how to shape their arguments. Too little demand undoes the purpose of a project: too much can destroy it.

5. The anaesthetists and the patient activists had interests (stakes) in their own achievements as doctors or as patient activists. They had to consider the probable reactions of their peers, known or unknown. Invisible bonds of accountability to those outside the working group spurred on the patient activists but tended to rein in the anaesthetists.

Two explicit principles guided the writing: that information should support patients' autonomy and that patients should not be patronised, that is, treated kindly but as an inferior (Lack, 2003). But exactly how these principles should be expressed through words was often disputed. Almost every word in *Anaesthesia explained* was debated, sometimes in meetings, sometimes by e-mails (Lack, 2003). When, rarely, consensus could not be reached, compromise was adopted as an almost-last resort. As a very-last resort, the topic was omitted from the text (Parroy et al., 2003).

Controversial points

Most controversial points were satisfactorily resolved. A few were not. The patient activists wanted a word to replace 'sleep' for the state induced by general anaesthesia. They thought 'sleep' inaccurate, misleading, patronising, and perhaps frightening for any child whose pet had been 'put to sleep.' In the end, 'controlled unconsciousness' was accepted by everyone, although no-one liked it. (The 2015 revision uses 'anaesthetic unconsciousness', which is better but too clumsy to be perfect.)

Another controversial point was whether the patient's anaesthetist should tell the patient his or her status in the medical hierarchy – consultant, registrar, etc. Hospital doctors and GPs are often reluctant to tell patients this when they introduce themselves. Doctors deem 'doctor' sufficient. Patient activists think that the status of the doctor treating them should be explained to patients. It could affect their consent to, or refusal of, treatment. They also need to know for ordinary conversation with their doctors, yet asking directly can seem unfriendly. The anaesthetists were not persuaded to change their view. But they suggested a proviso, that *Anaesthesia explained* could advise patients to ask to see a consultant, if they wanted to. Though this did not satisfy the patient activists, it could at least alert patients to a course of action they could take.

Disagreements occasionally caused angry feelings between patient activists and anaesthetists. But the patient activists valued the anaesthetists' generous intentions, integrity, and hard work. The anaesthetists valued the patient activists' good will, insights, and hard work. They liked the patient activists' explanations of the reasons for their views. These sometimes inspired them to change their own practices. That was never the patient activists' intention. They were working as equals, not as reformers. But they were pleased.

In the end, everyone was reasonably happy with the published result.

Changes to later editions

Anaesthesia explained went into its 5th edition in 2015. The latest edition has mostly kept the order of contents and often repeats sentences or paragraphs from the original, 2003, edition. It provides much more information, adding new material. It updates old information when practice has changed. It gives electronic links to further information. Colour photographs enliven it. These are improvements. But its tone has changed. These changes are sometimes subtle and I give four examples so that readers can compare the 2003 and the 2015 texts.

1. Introducing anaesthesia

2003: *If you have ever had a dental injection in your mouth or pain-killing drops put in your eyes, you already know important things about anaesthesia :*

* *It stops you feeling pain and other sensations.*

* *It can be given in various ways.*

* *Not all anaesthesia makes you unconscious.*

* *It can be directed to different parts of the body.*

This builds on patients' experience and knowledge. Even if they have not had either of these procedures, patients can quickly grasp what is being said because it is described in familiar and concrete terms. This can reassure them about their ability to cope with what is to come and can help them take part confidently in discussions with their anaesthetist.

2015: *This [booklet] is a good place to start in gaining some understanding of treatment that may be offered by your anaesthetist.*

The words 'understanding' or 'understand' are always risky: red lights should flash from them, whenever they are proposed. They can come across as demeaning, 'you don't know anything but we do' or even 'me clever, you stupid'. The phrase 'start in gaining some understanding' takes for granted that patients know nothing. That is not always true. Patients who do know something may find the phrase insulting.

2. **Choices of anaesthesia and of pain relief**

2003: Every choice that might be possible for some patients is flagged up by a symbol, a small weighing balance, in the margin of the text.

[symbol of small balance] *If you are having a regional or local anaesthetic, you may want to ask for some sedation as well.*

2015: The choices are in the text but not flagged up. Sometimes they are indicated so indirectly that they would be easy to miss.

Many people having a local or regional anaesthetic do not want to be awake for surgery. They choose to have sedation as well.

3. **What factors will determine what choices your anaesthetist will offer and will discuss with you**

2003: *The choice of anaesthetic depends on:*

★ *your operation*

★ *your answers to the questions you have been asked*

★ *your physical condition*

★ *your preferences and the reasons for them*

★ *your anaesthetist's recommendations for you and the reasons for them*

★ *the equipment, staff and other resources at your hospital*

This would be a model list for many specialties besides anaesthesia.

2015: *Sometimes there is a choice about which kind of anaesthetic and pain relief is best for you. Having talked about the benefits, risks and your preferences, you and your anaesthetist can decide together which anaesthetic you will have.*

This is good; but the 2003 version is better. The last reason in the 2003 edition is especially important. Patients need to know about constraints on their treatment and care, so they can either change to another hospital, if they think that prudent and practicable. Or accept them as part of their informed consent. Or decline the operation and anaesthetic, if they think the risks are more than they can bear (Wang, 2007).

4. Technical terms

2003: In explaining the apparatus anaesthetists use to monitor patients' physiological state during operations, the description and purpose of the *electrocardiogram, sphygmomanometer and pulse oximeter* are written in plain English followed by their technical names in brackets.

2015: The same three monitors are described but their technical names omitted.

Yes, plain English should be used. But patients and doctors can mean different things by some words and patients who want to take part in rational conversation with their doctor can find using exact terms helpful. Hospitals are like foreign countries – you have to speak a little of the language if you want to get the best from them.

Comparing *Good Medical Practice* and *Anaesthesia explained*

In contrast to *Good Medical Practice*, the later editions of *Anaesthesia explained* are less patient-aligned than the first edition. The latest edition provides more information to patients. But this is partly offset by the subtle changes to the text. 1. and 4. above are patronising. 2. and 3. are repressive. Both make it harder for patients to think about what choices they would want to make when opportunities for choices arose.

Regressive or backward changes are common in human affairs. Doctors have the power to ignore what they dislike or feel uncomfortable with. Civil rights activists and feminists know well how long it can take for changes that seem to be accepted to be put into wide practice. They also know how transient changes can be. Time moves on. Here both the anaesthetists and patient activists were different in 2015 from 2003.

Conclusion

Being politically aligned with doctors is the 'natural' state for both doctors and patients. Dominant interest-holders' interests dominate because both the stronger and the weaker groups accept them, accept the status quo. Getting dominant interest-holders to accept patient-aligned ideas, proposals, and words takes energy, determination and persistence. But a great deal can be done by patient activists and patient-aligned doctors working together. Separately, too, patient-aligned patients and patient-aligned doctors can influence other doctors and other health professionals in ways difficult to trace but cumulatively significant. The perspectives of doctors and of patients are far from integrated. But that may not be the best goal to aim for: reaching agreed courses of action may be better (Chapter 6).

Chapter 5

Enter managers

Our bureaucrats have minimised relationships with clients instead of maximising them.

BBC4 *Today* Programme 11th March 2013.

Introduction

When patient activists began to challenge standards of care in the 1960s, they talked to doctors, ward sisters, midwives, the medical royal colleges, and government officials. They were the people who mattered. Lay administrators organised hospitals and GPs' surgeries to support clinicians' work. But administrators never tried to influence clinical care; and sometimes they let non-clinical care – helpful daily routines, decent surroundings, palatable food – fall below acceptable standards, as at Normansfield Hospital (Department of Health and Social Security, 1978). This changed in the 1980s and 1990s when governments in the Western world began to promote managerialism in public services (Komesaroff et al., 2016). (Management is a skill, managerialism an ideology, managerial an adjective from either. Bureaucrats sit at desks, in French bureaux, and act managerially.) Managerialism has many definitions and ways of working (Klikauer, 2015). In healthcare, it aims to secure reasonable standards of cost–effective care for defined populations of patients. To do this, it seeks to control clinicians' practice (doctors and other clinical staff), making them accountable for their work and measuring it (Wikipedia, *Managerialism*, January 2017). Lay managers, exercising new powers under government departments of health, replaced lay administrators and tried to bring about this control (Harrison and McDonald, 2008). Civil servants and top managers, following governments' policies, introduced business-style management into the health service so successfully that it now seems 'natural' (Learmonth and Harding, 2004). This has made healthcare more prone to conflicts amongst all those who work for it. Patient activists may find that they have to talk with two sets of people, managers and doctors or other health professionals, not just one (Williamson, 2008). One for the price of two.

This chapter looks at managerialism; compares managerialists', clinicians', and patients' interests; and discusses two problematic aspects of managerialism in daily practice, the Quality and Outcomes Framework (QOF) and the managerialist value, efficiency.

Managerialism

The American physician, Dr Donald M. Berwick, head of the Institute for Healthcare Improvement in Cambridge, Massachusetts, says that the that the era of medical professionalism has given way to the era of managerialism (Berwick, 2016).

Managerialism is the opposite of professionalism. Professionalism focuses on individual patients and on relationships with them. *...Physicians and patients [should] engage in mutually rewarding relationships that do not sacrifice the patient's autonomy, the physicians's integrity, or medicine's goal of beneficence* (Brett and McCullough, 1986). Managerialism's focus on populations and its attempts to control doctors' work has positive and negative consequences for patients. It tries to re-balance doctors' tendencies to skimp care for disadvantaged social groups while spending more resources on fortunate groups; to promote standard treatments, eliminating wide variations between doctors' practices; and to keep the cost of healthcare from rising beyond the inclination of governments and insurance companies to pay for it. It does not concern itself with individual patients. They may or may not fit into the 'right' category or benefit from the standard treatment. Its focus on populations can put individual patients at risk. By contrast, doctors' focus on their own patients can put populations at risk. When managerialism was introduced into the NHS, many doctors seemed not to have realised how its beliefs and set of ideas (ideology) conflicted with theirs. Other doctors did; and doctors and managers sometimes struggle over specific issues (Hunter, 2006).

Managers in NHS trusts in England are themselves ever more tightly controlled by the party politicians in the government of the day: they now have less autonomy over their work than other professions in the NHS (Gillespie 1997). It is difficult to separate managerialism and managers from the party political context in which they work. '[Managers] are little more than conduits for the policies of the centre' (Blackler, 2006). This is stressful for senior managers, who 'are not really managers, because the politicians won't let them manage' (McCoubrey, 2019). Whatever the ideas of ever-changing Secretaries of State, managers must carry them out.

Locally, the exact balances of power between doctors and managers vary with circumstances. Their political relationship is now more a liaison than a struggle. In hospitals, executive managers' attempts to manage or control doctors and other clinical staff can leave them little political capital to draw for dealing with other demands and problems. These include patient activists' criticisms and requests for changes in policies and practices (personal communication, Dr Peter Kennedy, Chief Executive, York Health NHS Trust, 1997).

For general practice, GPs in York tell me that some of their younger colleagues hardly distinguish between managerialism and professionalism. Or if they do, they feel so despondent and helpless that they accept managerialism without protest (personal communications, 2016, 2018). Another GP, Dr John Goldie, has written that in the last 20 years, general practice's identity, structure, and practices have been transformed for the worse (Goldie, 2014).

Consequences for patients

It's hard for patients to disentangle the sources of policies or practices they hear about or experience. Did they come from their GPs' surgery, the local trust, the clinical commissioning group, NHS England, the Department of Health? Within the doctor–patient clinical relationship, patients can't tell whether their doctor is acting from professional ethics and clinical knowledge and acumen; or from subservience to management; or from convinced conversion to managerialism.

In addition to this uncertainty, the patient-aligned versus patient-non-aligned variable comes into play. Some managers, like some doctors, are patient-aligned, that is, they try to introduce higher standards of care that support patients' autonomy. The chief executive in York Health Services Trust introduced long visiting hours (support); set standards for how patients should be spoken to (respect); and monitored surgeons' morbidity and mortality rates (safety). Managers can use surveys to elicit samples of patients' experiences and judgments. (Measuring is a managerial tool and often useful.) They can then use the results to try to change institutions' and professionals' ways of doing things.

Or, like some doctors, managers can be patient non-aligned. They may oppose doctors closing wards to stop infections spreading because closing wards loses money (junior doctor, personal communication, 1995); press doctors to meet financial targets by reducing the time they spend treating patients (Mid Staffordshire NHS Foundation Trust Inquiry, 2013); turn a blind eye to doctors' poor clinical results (Bristol Royal Infirmary Inquiry, 2001) or even to deliberately shortening patients' lives (Gosport,

2018); run wards with too few nursing and ancillary staff (Mid Staffordshire NHS Foundation Trust Inquiry, 2013). They have pursued managerialist targets that can make staff feel pressured, even bullied. Pressure can lead staff in hospitals to take short cuts that deviate from good care but become accepted within the ward (Barach and Phelps, 2013). The harms that managers have done are recounted in reports of inquiries into hospital scandals like those above. The good is less often noted.

Signs of patient-alignment or patient non-alignment can be seen in general practice as well as in hospitals. A posy of garden flowers on the GPs' receptionists' counter symbolises patient-alignment, for flowers give pleasure to patients as well as to the receptionists themselves. Magazines banned from the waiting room, on the grounds of infection, symbolise patient non-alignment: official guidance on preventing the spread of infections in GPs' waiting rooms says that magazines are allowed (Harrogate and District NHS Foundation Trust, 2017). The medical anthropologist, Simon Cohn, discussed the widespread banning of flowers from general wards in hospitals, although there is no microbiological evidence that vases of flowers cause hospital-acquired infections. He suggested that decisions that contradict scientific evidence are based on values, not facts. Here technical efficiency, bureaucracy, and accountability for getting quickly through work has won over personal relationships and humane care (Cohn, 2009). Getting rid of harmless customs that have brought relief and pleasure to generations of patients is sad as well as misguided. Managerialism has taken effect, like bindweed smothering garden plants.

Managerialists', clinicians', and patients' interests compared

Table I. compares some of the broad values and interests of managers, doctors, and patients as they were in 2008 (Williamson, 2008). Some of the effects of managerialism on patients and their interests have been good, as patients and patient activists would judge them. Clinical audit; emphasis on socially disadvantaged groups of patients; trying to secure equity of provision for populations of patients, are probably more due to managerialism than to professionalism (Williamson, 2008). But some of the effects of managerialism have acted against patients' interests. Two are especially fraught with problems for patients: doctors' loss of some clinical autonomy, which risks jeopardising patients' autonomy; and the pursuit of efficiency at the expense of other values. I discuss them later in this chapter.

Mangerialists	Clinicians	Patients
Rational, that is, planned and efficient use of resources	Resources according to professional-defined need	According to need as defined by doctor and patient
For populations of patients	For individual patients	For both populations and individuals
Economic efficiency the goal	Quality the goal	Quality the goal but quality includes some efficiencies
Aim to reduce professionals' discretion as much as possible, to maximise efficiency and predictability	Professionalism intrinsically at odds with managerialism	Not known but doctors more trusted than managers
Control of clinicians' patterns of working	Free to work as think best, control over own work	Probably managerial control over patterns of working but not over clinical decisions
Abolition of clinical autonomy	Preservation of clinical autonomy	Preservation of clinical autonomy
Replacement of highly-qualified professionals with cheaper ones	Resist or doubtful about such replacements	Problematic
A small number of highly qualified professionals to become consultants to other staff	Highly-qualified professionals in direct relationships with patients	Highly qualified professionals as consultants to patients
Guidelines and protocols compulsory	Guidelines and protocols discretionary – essence of professionalism is knowledge and judgment	Guidelines and protocols to be offered to patient, then shared decision-making
Promote information and choice for patients	Slow to offer information to patients	Value full information, choice of treatment
Support innovation	Clinicians often resistant to change	Support innovation in response to patients' views and requests
Regulation heavy, managers and lay people in majority	Regulation light, professionals predominate	Regulation heavy, should include lay people
Belief in money as motivator	Belief in altruism as motivator	Probably both, like most people

Table 1.

Table 1. Managerialists', clinicians', and patients' values and interests compared, 2008

Reprinted from Williamson C. 'Alford's theoretical political framework and its application to interests in healthcare now', *British Journal of General Practice* 2008; 58; 552: 512-516, by kind permission of the Editor. The references are there. See https://bjgp.org.

The table shows how patients' interests (the stakes they hold in what they value, Chapter 1) zig zag between managerialists' and clinicians' interests. Patients' interests are like a river flowing into the sea between sandbanks at an estuary. Small shifts in the sandbanks can sometimes be brought about locally. A major re-configuration of the estuary requires either a storm at sea or a rise in sea level. Hospital scandals in which both ordinary social values and professional standards are breached; new compulsory national standards; or a new Secretary of State, can re-configure the estuary.

Patients' autonomy and the Quality and Outcomes Framework

Respecting people's autonomy means upholding their opportunities and abilities to act in accordance with their own moral and cultural values, their responsibilities to themselves, to their families and to their communities, and their interests as they define them (Chapter 2). In making clinical decisions, patients' autonomy requires that they be free from coercion, whether hidden (covert) or obvious (overt). Their doctors, too must be free from coercion; free to explore their own and their patients' perspectives – 'this is how I see things'– values and anxieties; free to discuss clinical evidence; and free to discuss all possible courses of action (including those not provided locally) with their patients (Williamson, 2005). Many clinical decisions that doctor and patient make together or that the patient freely delegates to the doctor rely on this freedom. No-one has unlimited autonomy or freedom to act as they choose in any aspect of life. The law and society's norms stop most people from driving through red traffic lights or stealing flowers from public parks. Clinical autonomy, too, has boundaries. Those boundaries can change with new medical knowledge and new social norms. But doctors' bounded clinical autonomy supports patients' autonomy. Limitations on doctors' autonomy, imposed by managerialists and accepted by doctors, risk impairing patients' autonomy (Williamson, 2003).

The Quality and Outcomes Framework (QOF), introduced into general practice in 2004 through the new General Medical Services Contract, constrains this freedom for some common clinical decisions like treatments for high blood pressure, high cholesterol levels, diabetes, asthma (Roland, 2004; Wikipedia, 2018). These decisions are made within the doctor-patient clinical relationship, so how they are made is fundamental to Medicine as a political, social, and moral enterprise.

The QOF rewards with money GPs' practices for patients' decisions that comply with specific courses of action determined by the government. (The financial reward is called an incentive or, less politely, a bribe.) It integrates government policy and clinical practice, potentially reducing professionals' discretion (Forbes et al., 2016). In addition, it potentially introduces bias into the consultation. Doctors should, and often do, provide patients with information about the range of treatments possible for their diagnosed condition. That information should be unbiased about the benefits and risks of each treatment (General Medical Council, 1995). This is for the patient's safety – the patient may know of other harms from the treatments – as well as from respect for their autonomy. Doctors can then give their patients advice about which clinical action might be best for them. But the QOF has introduced hurdles into this familiar course that doctor and patient run together.

First, unless the doctor tells the patient about the money gain to the practice, silence becomes secret coercion. The doctor may think that the rewarded treatment is the best treatment for this patient. But that does not justify silence. That was shown in the early days of patient activism when activist groups opposed clinical silence and its coercive power (Chapter 2). Secrecy has also been condemned in official inquiries into hospital scandals like Alder Hey and Bristol. (Royal Liverpool Children's Inquiry, 2001; Bristol Royal Infirmary Inquiry, 2001). These reports were published and got much public attention just before the QOF was discussed in the British Medical Association (BMA) and the Royal College of General Practitioners (RCGP). The reports' warnings against secrecy could have been heeded. They were not. This an example of a powerful group not bothering with what other people say, perhaps not even noticing it (Chapter 1).

The doctor may be tempted not to tell patients about the rewards to the practice. Not telling would save time. It would avoid patients' surprise or their critical comments. How far GPs are aware that their silence is coercive is unclear. Lack of awareness of how their actions or lack of actions can do harm is typical of powerful interest-holders (Chapter 1). The toad beneath the harrow suffers while the farmer gains ridges of fresh fertile earth. The farmer does not even think about the toad.

Second, the QOF recommendations apply to populations, not to individual patients. That is fine, provided that doctor and patient check that the recommended course of action is also the best one for the patient. If a population measure can have no ill effects on the patient, he or she should be offered the opportunity to accept it altruistically. This was established by the Inquiry into Alder Hey Hospital's practice of removing dead children's organs for study and research to benefit future children, without giving parents the opportunity to make that precious gift themselves (Royal Liverpool Children's Inquiry, 2001). Powerful groups can act high-handedly −'we know best' - as well as secretly.

When these ethical requirements are not met, the QOF becomes strongly coercive. It breaches the ethical value of lucidity, the requirement to tell patients about any factors that could affect the clinical decisions they make with their doctor (Fried, 1974). Papers reporting research into the QOF seldom or never mention whether patients knew they had personally been treated under a QOF protocol for their disease or, if they did know, what they thought. (This is like researching marriage by interviewing only husbands.) When I talked to patients about the QOF, I seldom found any patient who did know (Williamson, 2017). When GPs accept the QOF, they knowingly relinquish some of their own autonomy (Williamson, 2015). But they seem unaware − or don't care - that they risk undermining their patients' autonomy. We are all free to relinquish our own autonomy but not other people's. The doctors' leaders at the Royal College of General Practitioners and the British Medical Association who accepted managerialist proposals in the run up to the 2004 contract did not think of this (Williamson, 2017).

The QOF is an entirely managerialistic project. It undermines doctors' professionalism. Professionals can be paid for specific actions they have taken. GPs are used to a fee-for-services system. Patients who use private healthcare expect to get a bill afterwards, for their insurer or themselves to pay. When a public health measure, like vaccination or screening, is offered, people can (usually) decline to take part. But paying doctors to persuade patients, when they are ill or fear they might be ill, to accept a specific treatment is different. It can only be justified if the patient knows and accepts that the doctor will gain from their acceptance. If the patient does not know this, the QOF alters the doctor-patient clinical relationship by reducing doctors' trustworthiness, as patients would see it. But even when patients do know, they may refuse the specific clinical action and seek one that is unrewarded. They think it will be less biased. Or they want to show their disapproval of the scheme (Williamson, 2017). Conversely, some patients might be pleased to know that their GP was following official guidelines. Secrecy is never simple and seldom morally right.

GPs do not have to take part in the QOF, though 98% of practices do (Forbes et al., 2016). Their incomes partly depend on it – by 20% in 2012 (Hannon et al., 2012). From their incomes, GPs have to run their practice, provide its premises, and employ its staff, as well as paying themselves as partners (Misselbrook, 2011). Seven out of eleven practices advertising in the *British Journal of*

General Practice for July, 2019 for GPs to join them, listed 'high QOF achieving' as an attraction. The rest probably took part but chose not to highlight it.

Secrecy is not inherent in the QOF. Patients can study the QOF on the internet or track down research papers on it – if they have heard of it. Unfortunately, neither the Royal College of General Practitioners (RCGP) nor the British Medical Association (BMA) nor the Department of Health made frankness to patients a requirement of the QOF. The Patient Liaison Group at the RCGP was not consulted in the run up to the scheme nor represented on the group of GPs that negotiated with managerialists. In the words of its chair at the time, Joy Dale, the group was 'not allowed' to comment on the principles and proposals for the QOF (personal communication, 2006). We don't know what difference consulting the group would have made. It would probably at least have picked up the QOF's worst point: that GPs could keep it secret from their patients. The dismay, loss of trust, and contempt that some patients feel when they realise that they have been treated according to it, without being told, testifies to this ethical breach (Williamson, 2017). Secrecy has repressed patients' interests on a vast and tragic scale.

The pursuit of efficiency

Everyone wants well-run services that make prudent use of resources of all kinds (money, time, equipment, and so on); that provide congenial working conditions for doctors and staff; and clinically-competent, convenient, comfortable, and caring care for patients. But the managerialist pursuit of efficiency can conflict with these four c's.

Some GPs' surgeries show how this happens. GPs' surgeries vary, but a general practice surgery should be a symbol of reassurance, reliability, and kindness in the community of which it is a part. It should embody the virtues of Medicine itself. A trend towards larger surgeries, amalgamating branch surgeries or even combining different GPs' practices has been encouraged by the government. Very large GP practices with many GP partners and salaried doctors can act against patients' interests by making their visits to the practice impersonal and uncongenial. Although patients can still usually see the doctor they prefer, continuity of care can be disrupted if appointment systems do not allow patients to see that doctor reasonably quickly. High levels of continuity of care from GPs or from hospital doctors are associated with lower mortality rates (Pereira Gray et al., 2018; Baker, 2020). So constantly disrupting it matters. Some GPs value long, continuous relationships with their patients, and think that losing them would lessen their job satisfaction and general practice's ability to recruit new GPs (Salisbury, 2019). Early in the last century, GPs tried to prevent patients from changing their doctors within a practice: now they seem unable to help patients stay with the one they prefer.

A large practice also lacks the intimacy of a small one, where the patients, the doctors, the nurses, and the receptionists know each other, often well. In a small practice, even if the patient cannot see his or her preferred doctor, the others are not total strangers. Moreover, in a large practice, doctors may not have their own consulting rooms. The sense of security that a familiar base conveys, perhaps to the doctors themselves, certainly to the patients, is lost. Instead, doctors take turns with rooms. Each consults in an impersonal, standardised, room. None bears any reflections of the doctor – a family photograph, a picture of a favourite animal, a poster that livens up the wall. (These tell patients about the doctor as well as providing a bridge from social to clinical conversation.) A doctor may consult in a different room each time and, though the rooms may look the same, people have a spatial sense that tells them when rooms are in different positions.

In one surgery that merged two branch surgeries and the practice's headquarters into one building, the architect put the waiting room for patients in the centre of the building. The clinical, managerial, and administrative staff, rightly, have rooms with windows. Comfort and privacy are important for everyone. But the patients' waiting room has no windows. Each consulting room has a window, but as they look straight onto a car park, their blinds are kept closed. Once patients enter the surgery, they get no glimpse of the outdoors – no sky, no vegetation, no normal human activity passing by, not even a sight of a prowling cat or a dog on a lead - to break tension and reduce anxiety. The practice manager is proud of the 'state of the art' building with 'purpose built features for patients.' (*Practice News*, July 2018). Alas, it is an example of managerialist insensitivity to patients as sentient beings.

GPs' surgeries are not mini-hospitals and should play to their own potential strengths: good clinical and personal relationships; local knowledge and concern for neighbourhoods; kind and thoughtful care for everyone, patients and staff, alike.

Systems, like premises, can be impersonal, inconvenient, and hard-hearted. GPs' appointment systems are managed by the practice manager. Some appointment systems require patients to ring up at certain times only, so directly competing with other patients trying to get through on the telephone. Or patients are expected to use the practice's electronic site. (10% of the population can't use e-mail, *The Times*, 2019.) Or appointments can be made no longer ahead than a week, by when the preferred GP may have been fully booked. Although a scarcity of GPs has led to this rationing by delay and disappointment, better, less antagonising, ways could be found.

The pursuit of efficiency can also damage treatment. A recent study found that some GPs usually conducted reviews of elderly patients' medicines without inviting the patients to take part, although the guidance from NICE (The National Institute for Health and Care Excellence) recommended that patients be 'involved'. The patients' medicines were reviewed without them: their experiences and views were not sought. The GPs hesitated to remove medications perhaps no longer needed because that would involve discussing that with the patient (Duncan et al., 2019). The authors entitled their study 'Efficiency versus thoroughness in medication review'. It was worse than that. It was an example of poor clinical care and of poor ethical conduct. The patients should have been invited to take part in decisions about themselves and their care. They were treated as if they were receiving degrees, in absentia, at a university ceremony they had chosen not to attend. But they had not had that choice and knew nothing of their review.

Hospital doctors, too, have accepted elements of managerialism that act against patients' interests. Long waits in out-patient departments predate managerialism and have not disappeared with it. (Why not? Managers should be able to manage appointments systems.) Fleeting encounters with consultants on in-patient wards; ever-changing teams of junior doctors whose knowledge of the patients may be confined to a hurried read of their notes; in-patient stays sometimes too short (they used to be too long); too few beds, seem to be due to this acceptance. The old poor law approach to patients, from before the creation of the NHS in 1948, has been given new life by costly economies and inefficient efficiencies. One patient, recovering from a hip operation, was moved between wards seven times in his stay of three weeks, twice in the middle of the night (2019). Another, recovering from a fractured skull, was so kept awake by the cries of her ward-mates with dementias that she slept on two chairs in a day room down the corridor (2017). If value for money is a principle in hospital management, who is paying, in what currency, and for what?

In hospitals, staff in the emergency department and doctors on the ward try to gain patients' consent to medications (They have to for injections or other invasive procedures, otherwise those would count as assault.) But routine, short-term medications, laxatives for example, are sometimes given without discussion; without the Patient Information Leaflet that comes with every prescribed medicine (and could be photocopied when medicines are bought in bulk); and without the patient's explicit consent. Information about choices of possible medications may be limited, especially if a junior doctor is following a protocol and is not free (and perhaps does not know enough) to mention alternatives. Decisions may be made by doctors about what courses of action will or will not be taken for the patient, without his or her knowledge or consent. The patient may not even know that a decision is being taken, one to which he or she might want to contribute. To discover those decisions, patients can to ask for their medical or nursing notes after leaving hospital. They are sent, free of charge. Nevertheless, they are not in patients' hands when they need them most.

Pressures of work, lack of time, and too few staff are understandable reasons for these shortcomings. But some of them follow on from doctors' ways of controlling patients in the past, before shared decision-making was even thought of, and when the profession's power was supreme. Moreover, doctors have accepted managerialists' demands for efficiency – more work, less time, staff on shifts that prevent continuity of care for patients – without effectively opposing them. Nor have they publicised the breaches of standards and failures in care that have resulted (Chapter 6). Managers used to accuse doctors of 'shroud-waving', threatening that patients would die if more resources were not provided. Now doctors seldom wave more than a small blood-stained bandage. This restraint does disservice to patients. It does disservice to staff devotedly doing their best under poor conditions and harsh policies.

Active patients can sometimes protest against unsafe environments and skimped care, as they try to take control of their own treatment. They can alert staff to flaws and so indirectly benefit other patients (Chapter 3), though fear of reprisals can keep even active patients silent. 'Lying low and saying nothin'', like Bre're Rabbit in the tales from Afro-American folklore that the elderly freed slave, Uncle Remus, told of the Deep South US, is sometimes wisest

(Chandler Harris, 1886).

Some flaws could be mended by doctors themselves, if they paid more attention to the standards in *Good Medical Practice*. But junior doctors (doctors in training) may fear repercussions, damage to their careers, if they speak out (Brennan and Davidson, 2019). Blaming managers is always tempting. It is not always just.

Opposition to managerialism from patients

Patients and patient activists have been slow to challenge managerial actions. Managerially-directed actions that are designed to apply to populations of patients affect individual patients directly and are experienced by them personally. Doctors sometimes blur the distinction by, for example, inviting women to come for screening for breast cancer as if it were for their own sakes only, not primarily a population measure. Again, when doctors act as double agents, of the state and of the patient (Blomqvist, 1991 and Chapter 6), they seldom explain that they are constrained in what they can do. If patients see their doctor's action as harming them, they think the doctor responsible, not some manager or government official lurking invisibly in the background. Lack of openness hinders patients from understanding managerialism and managers' intentions and actions as well as they understand those of health professionals.

Opposition from doctors

From the early days of managerialism in the health service, a few doctors have argued against managerialist policies. In 2007, three years after the introduction of the QOF in the UK, two New Zealand GPs wrote an article entitled 'The Quality and Outcomes Framework: what have you done to yourselves?' In a perceptive analysis, they flagged up the QOF's threat to professionalism. They noted its potential damage to professional values and concepts of good care; its substitution through bribery of population medicine for personal care; its coercion of patients; its risk of loss of respect for doctors' and for patients' autonomy; its impairment of critical thinking and integrity; its damage to GPs' moral and legal legitimacy; its demotivation of doctors; its greater risk of undue influence from the pharmaceutical industry; and its loss of independence from the state (Mangin and Troop, 2007). Much of this has come to pass.

Research into managerialism and the QOF

Research has shown that some GPs have coerced patients into accepting treatments they had rejected (Checkland et al., 2008). Others regarded patients as 'walking bags of money' to be exploited (Norman et al., 2016). Seeing patients as if they were commodities worth money is how slaves were seen in the American South, or unmarried women with their dowries in Britain, in the 18th and 19th centuries. Instances of dishonesty and greed in modern Medicine may be rare. But the QOF lends itself to such conduct, especially through its secrecy.

Research has also shown that the QOF does little for patient-centred, integrated care. It may divert GPs from offering other aspects of high-quality care to other patients; there is no evidence that the QOF has improved the health of populations or reduced emergency admissions to hospitals (Forbes et al., 2016). When financial incentives were removed from specific clinical actions, GPs no longer recorded that they had implemented them. But they continued to record clinical actions for which incentives were maintained (Minchin et al., 2018). Combining professional and managerialist imperatives has not worked well. Repressing patients' interests has been pointless as well as unethical.

GPs occasionally write about their discontents. General practice no longer has scope for clinical thought and judgment (Heath, 2016); care is inhumane, paying little attention to the personhood of the patient (Dowrick et al., 2016); patientcare has become 'industrialised' (Lown and Peters, 2018); financial incentives have caused a needless professional crisis in medicine (McCartney, 2018). These criticisms seem to have made little difference in England or Wales. The Scottish health service has phased out the QOF (Forbes et al., 2016). The English and Welsh health services had seemed to be about to follow but have not done so. GPs have let their incomes be tied so tightly to their earnings from the QOF that reform is difficult.

Conclusion

Mangerialism's benefits and harms to patients, compared with Medicine's benefits and harms, need more analysis and discussion. Managerialism has some benefits for patients that are not dependent on saving money; and they need to be promoted (Chapter 6). Otherwise, managerialism will simply be seen as damaging dictatorships by managers intent only on saving money at the same time as, paradoxically, using money to control clinicians.

Managers and clinicians should work together (Greener et al., 2014). Yet when they do, there is a danger that they will act against patients' interests. Patient activists should always be invited to take part (or at least be allowed to take part, if they ask) in making decisions about managerial–professional policies. The repression of patients' interests has sometimes been inadvertent: it should no longer be deliberate.

Chapter 6

The political trio: patients, doctors, and managers

To say that [something] is apolitical...reflects a curiously narrow view of politics. Politics is found whenever there is a conflict to be resolved, and conflicts are a natural result of scarcities of goods and diversities of values - and cultures. Perpetuating a particular group, creed, or way of life is a political objective.

Lawrence Freedman, historian, 1993, p 7.

Introduction - emancipation revisited

Emancipation is a political concept, to do with power, who has it, who uses it and for what purposes. So it makes sense to fit it into a political framework. Several political frameworks have been proposed for healthcare. The one that I think best, that most closely describes and explains what we see in today's healthcare in the UK, was put forward by Robert R Alford, the American sociologist, in 1975. Patients' emancipation fits well into Alford's framework, though the idea of emancipation came into being much later (Preface and Chapter 1).

Emancipation movements seek equality of esteem, of voice, of influence, and ultimately of power between oppressed people and

107

the groups who oppress them. But they seek no harm to those groups or to their members. Emancipation movements are not revolutions, though they work for changes to social structures. In the women's and civil rights movements, one of the ways women and black, Asian and minority ethnic people can demonstrate equality with men and with white people is by succeeding at occupations and roles customarily held by them. That approach is not open to most patients. They have neither the wish nor the opportunity to become doctors. They have to develop and direct their capabilities in other ways.

In this chapter, firstly, I outline Alford's theory. Secondly, I compare the political positions of Alford's three major sets or categories of interest-holders today with what they were when he wrote about them in 1975. How much power, relative to the other two sets, do patients, doctors, and managers have now? Thirdly, I look at what individuals in each set of interest-holders could do to help the emancipation of patients, if they wanted to. (Some will not want to, Chapter 4). This book has mostly been about interactions between patients and doctors or managers. This chapter changes tack and sails along a less explored coast. This sail is fairly straightforward for patients. For doctors and for managers, it is more complicated. But I suggest that doctors and managers could take steps within their own professions, both to help patients' emancipation and also to relieve some of their own stress. Oppressing other people by repressing their interests may be convenient. But setting them free can free the oppressors.

Alford's theory

Social scientists agree that people connected with healthcare can be divided into three major sets or categories who have interests (stakes) in that healthcare: doctors, managers, and current and future patients. Social scientists hold different theories about the causes of this social and political pattern but Alford's theoretical framework is broadly accepted by UK social scientists. Many health professionals, including leading doctors in the medical royal colleges, have never heard of it. Nor have many patient activists.

Doctors and other autonomous health professionals, Alford said, held 'dominant interests' because their views of how patientcare should be provided usually prevail. Just as women have to live in a world suited to men, and in the UK and US black, Asian and minority ethnic people to white people, so patients have to enter a world suited to doctors. Doctors decide whether you have a disease; what tests should be done; what treatments might be effective; whether you see a consultant or a junior doctor; whether your GP visits you at home; and a host of policies and practices that most patients take for granted and seldom challenge. Dominant interests, ideas, and actions prevail because they are not widely criticised or opposed. (I make this point again because dominant interests seem 'natural'.)

Managers make up Alford's second category and the one he studied most closely. He saw them as holding 'challenging interests' because they challenge or oppose some of doctors' interests. Doctors are mainly concerned with individual patients: that lies at the heart of medical professionalism (Chapter 4). Managers are mainly concerned with populations of patients and the efficient use of resources (Chapter 5). Alford called managers and other people who share or support managerialism's values, 'corporate rationalisers'. He included health economists, public health doctors (as distinct from doctors in clinical practice), many academics, civil servants in government departments of health, senior managers, and deans of medical schools. In the UK, 'managerialists' is a more usual term than 'corporate rationalisers'.

Alford called patients and future patients, lay people in their communities or neighbourhoods, 'repressed interest-holders'. Their interests were repressed because they were threatened or kept down by the actions of the two other sets of interest-holders. Doctors and managers excluded them from important discussions. They kept some of their policies secret from them, deliberately or inadvertently. Doctors and managers were silent about their policies' implications or risks, again deliberately or inadvertently. That suppressed patients' interests. Sometimes patients could see how some professional or managerial policies and practices harmed them and their interests. But they were powerless to stop them or to change them. Their interests were oppressed. Suppression and oppression add up to repression (Williamson, 1992). (It's usual to speak of the oppression of women or of black, Asian or minority ethnic people or of patients because it's a useful general term.) Repressed interest-holders were little organised in the US in the 1960s. In the UK in the 1960s they were just beginning to form patient groups. Spokespeople for patient or community groups were, Alford said, easily diverted by doctors from speaking for patients' interests. This is still a risk in doctor-patient working groups.

Alford's focus on interests and interest-holders rather than on groups and members of groups is essential for his theory. It allows the members of one group to support the interests of another group over specific matters or controversial issues while still remaining members of their own group. We saw this freedom for interest-holders in Chapter 4, in some doctors' political alignments with patients. It underpinned the emancipatory sequence in maternity care, where a few obstetricians and midwives accepted women's pleas and changed their policies (Chapter 1). This ability of people to accept or adopt other people's interests allows changes of attitudes, norms, values, practices, and standards to take place. It is a general ability and gives hope to everyone who wants a better world, however they envisage that.

The interest-holders' political positions now

Patients' political position

Patients have come a long way politically since Alford published his book in 1975. Forming groups to take social action is a common first step in emancipation movements (Chapter 2). Patients have formed hundreds of patient groups in the US and the UK (Wood, 2000; Baggott et al., 2005). Many patient groups seek improvements to treatment and care for 'their' patients with specific diseases or conditions or in specific situations. Most groups declare themselves apolitical, and say they work cooperatively with health professionals (Wood, 2000). Claiming to be apolitical is a political statement: it supports the status quo, whatever the speakers' 'real' thoughts and motives. But the claim means that it can be hard for commentators and researchers to distinguish between radical or oppositional patient groups and the commoner conservative groups. Researchers' data and conclusions usually cover both. In any case, the groups' political alignments can overlap. So in this section I write about patients and patient groups generally, except when specifically referring to patients' emancipation.

Patient groups have prompted many changes to policies, practices, and standards (Wood, 2000; Baggott et al., 2005). Their members have served on professional or governmental working parties or committees. That is a major political advance: the first rule of politics is 'be there'. Another political step is to set up collaborative organisations to increase political impetus; and some patient groups have done that. Today, health professionals, managerialists, and politicians accept patient organisations, patient groups, and patients as part of the healthcare scene in the UK and the US. Managers and health professionals give some attention to their views, though not necessarily much (Wood, 2000; Baggott et al., 2005). Patient activists who are members of top-level government committees or working parties tend to find that the other members smile and say 'yes' but do nothing. Equality of voice is still often a distant vista. But compared with patients' position in the first half of the 20th century, these are striking political gains.

Patients or patient groups in the UK, however, have not always secured places wherever and whenever important national or local policies are made. They are still excluded from some decisions, though less often than in Alford's day. Nor have patient groups set up a national body in the UK that could take action through clear statements of position and careful arguments whenever issues pertinent to patientcare arose. Lack of social structures through which to mobilise patients' interests is another mark of the political weakness of patients and of the repression of their interests (Alford, 1975).

The creation of a national organisation that could reliably safeguard and promote patients' interests has been hindered by ideological differences and by lack of money. The Patients Association, founded in 1963, is a national charity that supports patients and provides them with information (Patients Association, *Patient Voice* 2019). Anyone can become a member, for free. It is a worthwhile organisation but not a radical one, and its political stance is heavily dependent on its chairs and chief executives. National Voices, founded in 2008, is a health and social care organisation that restricts membership to patient and social care groups (National Voices, internet, accessed September 2019). Individual activists cannot join; and some patient groups choose not to.

In 2009, a few patient activists got together to try to form a College of Patients. It was to be like a medical royal college, a place of learning, of setting standards, of discourse, debate, and of voice. The group quickly foundered for lack of money to pay simple expenses like rail fares to London, let alone for the sorts of prolonged meetings, discussions, and consultations that would have been necessary.

Difficulties for the patient movement as a whole, as well as for its emancipatory elements, abound. Many patients who join patient groups are transient, members only as long as they or their relatives are affected by their current healthcare. If the first rule in politics is to 'be there', the second rule might be 'stay there'. Some patient groups remain entirely voluntary, with no paid staff. This limits what the groups can do, though it gives them freedom to say what they like. If there are paid staff, tensions between volunteers and paid staff doing the same work but earning different rewards can arise, as they do in other organisations with volunteers and paid employees (Etzioni, 1961; Williamson, 2011). Even if the volunteers have other paid jobs (and some do not), a disparity remains.

Indeed, money is probably the most important factor in holding back the patient movement in the UK. Some patient groups accept money and help from pharmaceutical companies (Parker et al., 2019). Other patient groups shun that. They believe that it would compromise their independence and reputation. They look askance on patient groups who accept money or benefits in kind, just as some doctors look critically on colleagues who accept money or gifts from those companies. In the US, rich philanthropic individuals have founded and financed patient organisations like the Planetree Association in 1985 for personalized care and the Picker Institute in 1993 for patient-centered care (Martinsons, 1980; Picker, 2009). Both were founded by people who themselves or whose spouse had experienced poor care in the best American hospitals. Both promote good practice and high standards. Neither has emancipatory goals.

The patients' emancipation movement in the UK has shown slow and inconspicuous development. In the US the active patient, Dave deBronkart, is a spokesperson for what he calls 'a new social movement'. Its e-members (active patients, Chapter 3) want doctors to respect patients' autonomy and to recognise that the contributions of 'thinking patients' to their own treatment and care are necessary for the best possible care. Autonomy, emancipation, self-determination, knowledge, and responsibility are the movement's key words (deBronkart, 2015). It is a flamboyant version of the older and quieter British patients' emancipation movement.

Doctors' political position

When Alford published his book almost 50 years ago, doctors on both sides of the Atlantic were much stronger politically, more important, more influential, than managers. The rise of managerialism in the 1980s and 1990s changed that. Managerialists' challenges to doctors have been so successful that doctors and managers are now about equal in power, though varying with the circumstances and situations (Chapter 5). But one of the strangest things in the history of Medicine is doctors' uncritical acceptance of managerialists' power over them. The Irish gastroenterologist, Dr Seamus O'Mahony, wrote that the medical profession has 'sleepwalked' into ceding leadership to managers and to medical academics (O'Mahony, 2019). (His views are independent of Alford's, to whom he does not refer.) The metaphor fits because doctors have accepted many aspects of managerialism without thorough analysis or attention to its possible long term consequences. An example is GPs' acceptance in 2004 of one of managerialism's greatest political triumphs, the Quality and Outcomes Framework.

The sleepwalkers metaphor is good; but sleepwalkers usually harm neither themselves nor anyone else. Doctors can also be compared with walkers on a mountain, who reach the summit in golden sunshine. They feel exhilarated by the view, so glorious, so high above the tiny people in the valley below. Fog then blots out everything. The walkers had not bothered to take a map or a compass. (Why should they, in such sunny weather?) They are now in peril, stumbling down, not knowing how to find a safe way. Yet maps had been published years before – political and sociological maps, including Alford's. But Alford's theory has never caught on with UK doctors, who tend to disregard most academic disciplines or points of view except their own. In medical school, students may ignore or despise sociology and psychology courses (Sinclair, 1997). (Sinclair does not mention political science courses as even existing.) Yet Alford's theory, or some other relevant political or sociological theory, could help doctors choose their political positions and courses of action, their mountains and the paths up and down them, more carefully and more courageously. 'There is nothing as practical as a good theory' is a social science maxim. Even if a theory turns out to be partly or wholly wrong, clarity is better than muddle.

Lack of a practicable political theory has contributed to three confusing and difficult aspects of doctoring: muddled medical messages; doctors' double role; and doctors' moral distress.

Muddled medical messages

Muddle over who believes what shows in the manifesto for a 'new professionalism', written by a working party on modern medical professionalism at the Royal College of Physicians and published in 2005. It says that medical professionalism should be *based on an indissoluble partnership between patient and doctor in a radically new social context* p.10. It urges doctors to abandon, among other things, their clinical autonomy, autonomy within a clinical situation or relationship. It says that patients should be confident that when they consult a doctor, *the advice the doctor gives should be governed only by their interests and needs alone* p. 16; and declares that *Securing trust is the most important purpose of medical professionalism* p.15 (Royal College of Physicians, 2005).

Even within its clearly written text, the Report contradicts itself. If clinicians have given up their clinical autonomy, or some of it, their advice is unlikely to be determined only by their assessment of the patient's interests and needs (Chapter 4). The Report disregards its own statements about the resource components of medical decisions, managerial imperatives, and 'difficult choices'. 'Securing trust' cannot be the 'most important purpose of medical professionalism' unless the profession is subordinating all other purposes to it. As clinical decisions cannot always be governed by the patient's interests and needs alone, being trustworthy rather than securing patients' trust would be a more realistic professional purpose. The Report's statement that *Medicine bridges the gap between science and society* p. xi, is almost as fanciful.

How could a document from seventeen people, mostly eminent doctors, be confused? Of the seventeen members of the working

117

party, about half were clinicians and half were deans of medical schools or engaged in medical education. That is, the latter were medical managerialists. (Two or three members had other backgrounds, less easy to discern politically.) The document mentions discussion and dissent in the working party, but does not say what about. Judging by the references they cite, the members consulted no books or papers about healthcare politics. If they had read Alford's book, they could have seen that the working group contained clinicians and medical managerialists in roughly equal numbers. Then they could have drawn up a detailed comparison between the two sets of beliefs. They could have worked out a view of medical professionalism that weighed the relative importance of medical professionalism and of medical managerialism. That would have immensely useful to the profession and to patients. For want of a political nail – one crucial book on a library shelf - the shoe and then the horse were lost.

Patients' possible views were not mentioned. Patients do not want indissoluble partnerships; they want to be free to change their clinicians, if a clinical relationship or care is unsatisfactory. Even a collective partnership, a social contract, between clinicians and patients cannot be indissoluble because it would leave out the third major set of interest-holders, managers. In healthcare looked at politically, alliances repeatedly form, break down, and form again in new configurations amongst the three sets of interest-holders. This is why it is essential to include in every discussion or debate patient activists, active patients or general patients, as the nature and level of the discussion dictate.

Many patients know that their clinician's advice is likely to be influenced by several factors. They want to trust their clinicians' motives and their capabilities. But patients know that clinicians may sometimes act against their own or against other patients' interests, as they would define them . Trust is a personal and social good (Harrison and Smith, 2004). But it must be underpinned by openness and truthfulness.

Doctors' double role

Another political difficulty for doctors is their double role. The Swedish-American health economist, Åke Blomqvist, says that clinicians have become 'double agents'. They act as agents of patients who have an interest (stake) in doctors providing them with information and with medical services. They act as agents of those paying for these services, the state in the UK, insurers in the US, in economising in what they provide (Blomqvist, 1991). John le Carré's novels and the biography of the spy Oleg Gordievsky, who defected from Russia to the UK in 1985, show that being a double agent is exacting and stressful (le Carré,1974; Macintyre, 2018). You, the double agent, must never let slip that you are on the other side. You must get both sides to trust you. That trust is vital for carrying out your work and for preserving your life. (Is this why doctors put emphasis on trust, not on trustworthiness?) Double agents can become confused and emotionally torn between people they like on both sides. They can begin to lose their sense of their own identity. If they decide to defect, in which country should they seek shelter and safety? Doctors sometimes seem confused about the irreconcilable differences between the basic professional and the basic managerialist positions.

The English GP, Dr Julian Pratt, looked at the question of double agency in a different way, though he did not use the term (Pratt, 1995). He distinguished between practice (managerial) values and practitioner (professional) values. He suggested that individual GPs might choose to follow one or the other set of values, provided the practice contained both sorts of GP. Separating doctors in this way, across all specialities, would be impossible. There are not enough GPs or consultants to make it feasible, even if it were desirable. Yet the idea of doctors explicitly and openly separating professional and managerialist ideas in everyday medical work is good. Managers could do the same, saying when they were supporting professional ideas or supporting managerial ones.

Some of the stress doctors experience probably comes from their double agency. If being a double agent can be stressful for clinicians, being a patient who knows about double agency can be deeply disturbing. Some patients have long known that their doctors rationed treatment. They hoped that rationing would not put them at risk (Mechanic, 2004). Recent shortages of resources in the NHS may have removed that hope. A patient recently described to me how uncomfortable consultations with doctors now were. All the time she was wondering how far her doctor's advice was dictated by costs (Sheila Shinman, personal communication, 2019). Asking directly is awkward, for it in effect accuses the doctor of deceit. What is certain is that clinicians should tell their patients when costs become a factor in making a specific clinical decision (Kassirer, 1998). Telling patients would give some of them an opportunity to try to protect their health by paying for private healthcare or by moving to another part of the country or to another country. That these inequitable steps could be necessary shows how serious the present situation is in the UK.

Doctors' moral distress

Moral distress is the term for healthcare workers' feelings when institutional constraints, like lack of staff or lack of resources, prevent them from doing what they think is right for a specific patient or patients (Oliver, 2018). It was first identified (described and named) in 1984 among nurses. Doctors, porters, ward clerks and managers – all those in contact with patients - can also experience it. It is to the credit of staff that they feel distress when they cannot offer patients appropriate treatment and care. But health professionals have chosen to cope with their feelings through therapeutic group meetings (Oliver, 2018). They have not, it seems, always told the patients who are or who might be affected. The ethical value of lucidity, the right of patients to know about all the relevant aspects of their situation (Fried, 1974) has not been respected. Doctors have put other values above patients' autonomy and even above their safety. That deprives patients of the opportunity to seek other care. It also deprives doctors of the support they would get from patients and the public, if they made their difficulty widely known. In the QOF, doctors repressed patients' interests to suit their own interests. In keeping silent to patients about moral distress, doctors repress patients' interests to suit managerialists' or the government's interests. They also harm their own interests by helping to sustain an inadequately funded or poorly managed health service, so increasing their own stress.

Managers' political position

The rise of managers and of managerialism in healthcare, predicted by Alford, has been rapid since governments in western countries promoted managerialism. Governments once saw doctors as the means of securing healthcare for their citizens (Gillespie, 1997). Now governments have given that task to managerialists and managers.

Management comes in various forms. The emergence of commercial or market management can be seen in Mrs Gaskell's *North and South*. Factory owners separated themselves from their workers, 'hands', and sometimes treated them badly. They withheld information, gave low wages, and hired and fired erratically. They brought in soldiers or workers from far afield, if the 'hands' went on strike for better pay or working conditions. The owners did not respect the 'hands' as people like themselves (Gaskell, 1855). Seeing other people as inferior is a moral flaw; but it can feel justified to those who hold great power (Chapter 1).

Market managerialism was embraced in the 1980s by the UK government, even though the NHS was a public service. The Conservative prime minister, Mrs Thatcher, had high regard for a report by the managing director of a supermarket chain, Sainsbury's, Roy (later Sir Roy) Griffiths (DHSS, 1983, the Griffiths Report). The Griffiths Report was intended to promote efficient and humane healthcare (Griffiths, 1992). It partly failed, Sir Roy says, through misunderstandings, confusion, and too much intervention by Members of Parliament. It would have taken God more than six days to create the world, if backbench

MPs had been around (Griffiths, 1992). Misunderstandings and confusion often signal unrecognised conflicts. They should always be scrutinised. Those MPs may have been doing their proper work, protecting their constituents' interests.

After the Griffiths' Report, managerialists gained ever greater power in the health service, including over doctors (Chapter 5). Gradually, politicians in government (both Conservative and Labour) tightened their grip on managers. They eventually made the chief executive officers of trusts directly accountable to them via NHS England, the top NHS commissioning body for the NHS in England (Blackler, 2006). Party political managerialism reigns.

Executive managers at local level can feel oppressed by managerialists in NHS England and by politicians (Blackler, 2006). Doctors can feel oppressed by managers (Chapter 5). Patients can feel oppressed by doctors (Chapters 1 and 2). This is hardly a good way to run a health service.

Steps that the interest holders can take to help patients' emancipation

Steps that patients can take

Patients – whether radical or conservative patient groups, patient activists, active patients. or general patients – can take various steps to move patientcare towards higher standards of treatment and care and towards greater respect for patients' autonomy. These steps require them to use their capabilities. Not all patients want to or can do this. But social change requires only a minority of activists in a population (Chapter 2).

Major steps

1. Patients could form or join an actual or a virtual patient group, the unit of social support and of political action.

2. Patients who want to promote emancipation could join with others to draw up an ideology for the emancipatory part of the patient movement. That would flag up its guiding ideas, values, and hopes. Patients' autonomy and equality of esteem and of voice with doctors and other autonomous health professionals, and with managers, would be part of any ideological statement.

3. Patients (and health professionals and managers) should think and talk about standards of patientcare. Almost all episodes of patientcare contain both good and bad aspects, as patients experience and judge them (Goodrich and Cornwell, 2008).

Standards, defined in Chapter 2, can be of three major kinds:

i. Standards that breach ordinary social norms and ideas of humane conduct, the way people should behave towards each other. In our society, this includes never inflicting avoidable pain or distress on other people. Breaches should be easy to spot and to counter, using the 'ordinary' lay knowledge of our society's norms and values (Williamson, 2018). Staff and managers often do not act on such breaches (Goodrich and Cornwell, 2008; Mannion and Davies, 2019).

ii. Standards that have been accepted and promoted by authoritative bodies like the medical royal colleges and professional associations, that is, professional standards. These organisations should take into account standards patient groups or patient activists put forward to them. They do not always do this; but examples in Chapter 4 show that it can be done.

iii. Standards that patient-aligned health professionals or patient groups have put forward but that have not been fully accepted by authoritative bodies. If these standards point in the direction of privacy in place of its lack; comfort instead of discomfort; encouragement for patients' independence and autonomy instead of discouragement; attractive environments instead of bleak ones; flexible care instead of rigid routines; negotiable and consultative care instead of imposed autocratic care; individual instead of batch treatment; patients' easy access to friends and relatives at times of stress instead of restricted access; information offered in advance and during care instead of afterwards (or never); and personal instead of impersonal care, health professionals and managers are likely to accept them sooner or later (Williamson, 1987). More generally, standards that express the patient principles and that support patients' autonomy, are likely to be accepted in due course. Vistas may be distant. But they come into closer view as patient-aligned people walk towards them.

Patients can draw on all three sets of standards, as opportunities arise or can be created.

Detailed practical steps:

1. Patients could study the sets of standards in patient journals, professional journals and on the internet. Sometimes just pointing out breaches of them or opportunities for improvements to the local trust or GPs' surgery can set in train change. Praising specific aspects of patientcare, with reasons, is always worth doing. Good care deserves patients' approval and support.

2. Patients could welcome intuition and check it against standards. An intuition that something is wrong or is not quite right is an invaluable guide to action (Chapter 2). The more patients know about standards for patientcare, the keener their intuitions and the better they will be able to make sound judgments and to explain exactly why they judge care as poor or good. Early patient groups had little knowledge to draw on (Chapter 2). But now patients' new knowledge has spread and has influenced professional knowledge (Arksey, 1994). Sometimes a standard that seems necessary or desirable has not been formulated; it does not exist. Then a patient (or anyone else) can try to fill the gap and devise one: the actions identified and the values attached to them can come from any source.

3. General patients, as well as patient activists and active patients, can act on their experiences and judgments by writing reports on their stays in hospital or on episodes of GPs' care. Published reports of poor care abound. One from 14 years ago could have been written today. It describes 'never seeing a nurse except when drugs were being handed out, no one offering reassurance or information, days going by without any contact with senior medical staff, virtually having to beg for help moving up the bed or getting to the toilet, repeated requests for analgesia' (Teale, 2007). But in patients' published reports, the hospitals are seldom named. So it's easy for hospitals to think 'we're not like that'. Reports sent to the trust's chief executive or medical director or to the GP practice's senior partner are likely to have more effect. Sent to them not as complaints but as straightforward observations of poor and good care, reports can help them in their work for better patientcare. Though they should already know some of the shortcomings of situations or of staff, impetus from outside can help them take action.

If patients criticise, they can fear reprisal. This is a deep-seated and not wholly irrational fear (Morrison, 1994). The Gosport Inquiry reported that staff joked about putting obstreperous patients onto syringe drivers (devices that injected a continuous dose of medication into the patient's body) that delivered fatal doses of opiates (Gosport Independent Panel, 2018). But, once a patient has left the hospital or has recovered from the episode of the GP's care, fear of retaliation is probably manageable. Courage will still be called for. But courage is the capacity to deal with rational fears without letting them join with unconscious fears (Freud, Anna, 1965).

4. Medical journals like the *BMJ* accept articles from patients. The *BMJ* seems to like new insights from patients into matters for which there are no detailed standards. Then doctors can read the articles without feeling guilty. Criticisms of doctors' failures to practice to accepted standards are less likely to be accepted. But it's worth trying.

5. Reading patient groups' manifestos on the internet; consulting sites that give reputable clinical advice; and talking with other patients, can help patients take action. Patients may or may not see their actions as emancipatory or see themselves as joining an emancipation movement. This is partly because emancipatory patient groups have not fully articulated or declared their ideology. Or some patients may find the idea of emancipation too scary, too likely to alienate doctors. Others may just find the idea uncongenial. This is like other emancipation movements. They take time to mature and to become familiar to the rest of their society.

Steps doctors could take within their profession to help patients' emancipation

These steps are distinct from those individual patient-aligned doctors can take within their own everyday practices.

1. Doctors could discuss the conflicts between professional care for individual patients and managerialist care for populations of patients thoroughly, instead of just taking conflicts for granted. They could also examine their own support for the QOF, muddled medical messages, double agency, and moral distress. The medical

128

royal colleges are responsible for leading such discussions and for finding solutions. If solutions are impossible or imperfect for political or for pragmatic reasons, the profession must be open and truthful about it. Using the doctor-patient relationship as a means of rationing; or for imposing covert national or local policies; or for hiding deficiencies in treatment and care, is likely to destroy patients' and the public's trust in and esteem for doctors. That will lose doctors political support in any difficulties to come.

2. Lay people seldom mention doctors' deficiencies without hoping that medical students' training can be changed. The patronising baby talk that offends patients (Chapter 1) was formerly promoted in medical schools (Sinclair, 1997). But it lingers on. It should be dropped. It is discreditable in itself and harms relationships with patients.

3. Doctors' defence mechanisms need attention from doctors, patients, managers, and policy-makers. The most basic defence mechanism, avoiding feelings of disabling vulnerability, through psychological separation from patients, may be inherent in the doctors' task (Wessely and Gerada, 2013). But it can be recognised and buffered against. Avoidable stress on doctors should be avoided, through the organisational, environmental, and cultural improvements that doctors and their well-wishers propose. These include comfortable and private sitting or dining rooms, separate from patients and from other staff; hot food when on night duty; a return to 'firms' of consultant and junior doctors for better learning and support (McCartney, 2016; Rimmer, 2019; Elton, 2019). These are desirable for the doctors' own well-being, not just to help them behave more considerately towards patients.

Steps managers could take within their profession to help patients' emancipation

Local managers' primary responsibility is to manage the general environment within which healthcare is provided to the public (Blackler, 2006). Local managers have little autonomy and may be reluctant to allow autonomy to others (Gillespie, 1997). But they have scope for initiatives within their responsibilities: the administration of the trust or the GPs' practice; the quality of its environment; the soundness of its finances; and the use of language:

1. Administration requires more skill, energy, and attention to what's going on than it always gets. Any patient whose hospital notes are missing when they arrive for their appointment knows that. But administration is honourable as well as necessary work. Managers should try to ensure that all administrative systems and staff in their trusts or GPs' practices work accurately, promptly, and humanely.

2. The chief executive's or practice manager's responsibility for the environment of their institution includes physical and psychosocial environments, because they affect each other. Are notices helpful without being bossy? Are receptionists swigging from water bottles or munching apples in front of patients? Are letters written in plain and polite English? Are translations easy to get? Are flowers welcomed in general wards, not banned on the unscientific grounds that their water carries infection? Are the lavatories/ washrooms clean? Are their mirrors too high for short people to see themselves? Can they reach the paper towels or the air dryer without water running down their arms? Many

points like these will occur to anyone who has ever spent time in a hospital or in a GPs' surgery. Every aspect of the surroundings needs to be scrutinised for its symbolic meanings and messages as well as for its practical merits (Willliamson, 1992).

For inspiration, managers can look at the environmental practices and philosophies of American Planetree Association hospitals. Planetree hospitals pay attention to colours; pictures; low counters in out-patient departments; comfortable chairs; plenty of (real) flowers and foliage; choice of single or four-bedded rooms for in-patients; sitting rooms for patients and separate ones for nurses and for doctors; pleasant views from patients' windows; visiting at any time by friends and relatives; good food; easy-to-find information about diseases and treatments. Self-medication, when patients keep their medications by their beds and take them at agreed times, is standard practice. Patients can read their nursing and medical notes and can write in them. These steps show that patients are respected and valued (Martinsons, 1980; Gutstein, 1993).

Some steps like these cost money or need to be planned and negotiated with staff; but many do not. Some are in place in some UK hospitals and GPs' surgeries; but few are common. Changing environments and practices can be difficult, if that would interfere in staff's accustomed ways of doing things and their relationships with each other, with their culture (Mannion and Davies, 2018; 2019). But chief executives and other executive directors and heads of services are paid to do difficult things. Making hospitals and GPs' surgeries pleasant and supportive for patients and for staff would be a sure way of gaining their respect.

3. Financial matters. This is an exacting area of responsibility, partly because of executive managers' subordination to party politicians via managerialist civil servants and other government-appointed high officials. That subordination can prevent local managers from taking actions that suit the particular situations and aspirations of their hospitals or their GPs' practices. It can force them into taking actions of which they disapprove (Blackler, 2006). But as management develops its skills and managerialism becomes more widely understood, senior and executive managers should be able to engage with party politicians in ways that do not simply comply with their off-the-cuff ideas and their dangerous desires to make their personal mark on the NHS.

4. The rhetoric of management - words like empowerment, world class, vibrant, committed - are best avoided. They are often used without clearly defined meanings and can impair clear thinking (Loughlin, 2004). Alford thought that corporate rationalisers (managerialists) were cunning and deceitful, hiding their agendas under deliberate falsehoods (Alford, 1975). I think that managerialists feel reassured and supported by their own rhetoric, without noticing, or perhaps caring, that it is not always exact or credible. All managers need to guard against falsehood, for nothing is more discreditable in any profession. Some party politicians regard lying as part of party politics (Finklestein, 2019). This should never be allowed to infect the health service.

If the way of organising, governing or financing the NHS changes, managerialists and managers will still need independent judgment, initiative, and respect for everyone's autonomy.

Chapter 7

Concluding thoughts : a new model?

The aim of a life can only be to increase the sum of freedom and responsibility to be found in any man or in the world. It cannot be, under any circumstances to reduce or suppress that freedom, even temporarily.

Albert Camus, philosopher, 1961, p 241.

Introduction

Readers will have noticed that two themes come up repeatedly in this book: standards of treatment and care; and patients seen by doctors as 'non-people.' They are linked through patients' experiences and their interpretations of those experiences. Patients have felt belittled by some doctors' patronising behaviour towards them and failure to put into practice basic standards of courtesy. The patients wondered about those doctors' competence (Chapter 1). Patients can also interpret low standards of treatment and clinical care as due to health professionals' lack of respect or value for the patient's personhood. A mother whose newborn baby died, avoidably, from poor care, said 'he was a living person'. She believed that staff in the maternity unit had not seen him as such (BBC 1, February 13, 2020, 6 o'clock News). Hospital scandals like Bristol or Gosport showed care that disregarded both ordinary social values and norms and adequate professional or clinical standards (Chapter 5). Seeing standards and patients' personhoods as closely connected is important. Standards are simple to write about. 'Non-people' is complex. Streams in limestone districts can run partly over ground, light and clear, and partly underground, dark and mysterious. So it is with standards and patients as non-people.

Standards of treatment and care

Standards are straightforward to define and discuss (Chapter 2). To recapitulate, difficulties arise when people disagree about which actions should be subject to standards and what prescriptive values should be attached to those actions. It's easy to understand why doctors don't always follow high professional or clinical standards: loss of personal power; too little time; too busy; forget or overlook; unfamiliar; disapprove of; contrary to the norms of their colleagues; incompatible with the doctor's purposes. Professional or clinical standards that incorporate values that emancipatory patients and patient groups want to see in place, are particularly at risk. Even doctors whom patients think 'good' can unexpectedly breach professional standards. A doctor may fail to give information when a patient asks for it, a pathology report, say. Or omit to ask a patient for consent to a doctor in training operating on him or her.

Standards incorporating the patient principles and the professional principles for information and shared decision-making seem to be the most likely to be breached. Or patients may notice their breaches most readily. When they do, they may lose their esteem for the doctor.

Lay people and patients can understand breaches of standards because they are used to standards in ordinary life. Every social group has its customary and legitimate ways of doing things. Some of them it shares with other social groups; some are special to it. Children learn their social group's standards at home and in school. Doctors learn theirs at medical school and early practice. Both social and professional standards, values, and norms of behaviour can be changed in the long run. Emancipatory patient groups and patient-aligned doctors have done just that. Changes to professional standards have been stimulated, accompanied or followed by changes to social expectations of what those standards should be. This is how society works.

Patients not seen 'as people'

This is more difficult to define and discuss. Doctors themselves sometimes recognise it in themselves or in other doctors (Chapter 1). The idea of basic shared humanity – that all people are of equal worth – is so familiar to us that we can believe we feel it when we do not. That people can be blind to their words and actions suggests that many people do not 'really' feel that others are their equals.

Health professionals and patients writing about their own experiences can give vivid accounts of poor, impersonal or patronising care. But they seldom give enough social context to let the reader get the picture as persuasively as the writers would wish. The reader can't exclude the writer's peculiarities of personality or of situation. That can hinder readers from taking the writer's account to heart.

Literature, however, can show aspects of life more intensely, more accurately, and more subtlety than most autobiographical accounts or research findings. Fiction in which the author's experiences or observations are lit up by imaginative sympathy are especially telling. Poetry and fictional prose can give us deep understanding because great writers transfigure experience by their own vision (Cecil, 1956).

Literature can show how not seeing people as people is closely linked to oppressing them. The Russian novelist, Ivan Turgenev's, collected short stories, *A Sportsman's Sketches*, 1852, portrayed serfs as human so powerfully that it was believed to have influenced Tsar Alexander II, to liberate them in 1861 (Turgenev,1950). The American novelist, Harriet Beecher Stowe's novel, *Uncle Tom's Cabin; or, Life Among the Lowly,* 1852, helped towards the abolition of slavery in 1863 (Wikipedia, January 2020).

Fictional accounts can also tell of understanding, kindness, and love. Here are words from *War and Peace,* about an old lady with dementia: '[Her]condition was understood by all the household, though no-one ever spoke of it. [They knew] that she had done her work in life already, that she was not all here in what was seen in her now, they were glad to give way to her …for the sake of the poor creature, once so dear, once so full of life as they' (Tolstoy, 1925, p 1469). Quotations like this are probably more inspiring than exhortations to staff to show compassion.

Exactly why some doctors don't see patients 'as people' remains puzzling. Psychoanalytic theory about the unconscious; sociological theory about roles and relationships; religious tenets about sin; sociobiological observations about stronger individual animals dominating weaker individuals in the same species; capitalism and markets favouring the rich over the poor; theories of social stratification (class); power in all its aspects; and so on, have their place. Each can seem relevant in some ways or contexts; none can cover everything. In writing this book, I have come to think of 'situational power.' That combines doctors' power to act freely, to some extent, with patients' tendency to accept that power because they need the doctor's skill or advice or other help. But patients who oppose that power, individually in clinical relationships or collectively in social groups, are taking steps towards patients' emancipation, whether or not they fully realise and intend that.

The state of patients' emancipation now

When in the late 1950s, a few patients took their first scattered steps towards raising the standards of patients' care, they started an irreversible change of direction in healthcare. The times were propitious; those patients were ready; a tiny trickle of opposition became a stream. Patient activists have improved institutional and professional policies for patients in general. Active patients have improved their own treatment and care, with side benefits to other patients. But successful emancipation movements change societies. They make societies more humane and their members more equal. Can the patients' emancipation movement do this for the health service?

Creating a health service that would be more humane and whose members would be equal would be hard. It would require much thought, work, political skill, and good feeling. Patients are now seen as legitimate interest-holders. They have shown that they can set in train changes to patients' care, effectively and harmoniously. They have shown a commitment to improving patientcare, at least as dedicated as that of health professionals or managers. Some patient activists have worked for 40 or so years (usually without pay) to bring about changes to standards and attitudes, devising all sorts of strategies and trying various approaches. Patients have acquired and earned a voice.

Patients' emancipation could contribute to changing the health service in at least three ways:

1. It could offer a new approach to patientcare: the pursuit of greater freedom and responsibility for patients and for health professionals and for managers, within limits agreed by all three in tripartite discussions and debates. Those limits would remain open to new insights; new developments in clinical science and in management theory; changes in patients' experiences and sensibilities. All would be within the changing context of the outside world, itself influenced by changes in the health service.

Conflicts would take place as often, perhaps oftener, when each set of interest-holders felt free to put into words and to explore with the others, their ideologies, ambitions, and wishes. Consensuses strengthen the health service. But conflicts can sometimes be turned into consensuses. In the 1960s, mothers wanted to be allowed to stay with their children in hospital. Resistance from most nurses and paediatricians prevented it. A few paediatric nurses and paediatricians promoted it, against their colleagues' views – following this common pattern in emancipation movements. Patient activists enlisted their support. Once present on paediatric wards, mothers could feel awkward and nurses could feel jealous of the children's preference for their mothers (Isabel Menzies Lyth, psychoanalyst, personal communication, 1979). But nurses began to be glad to have a responsible adult on the ward, who could keep the child calm and happy. Paediatricians came to see that children recovered more quickly. Managers were freed from parents' complaints and could think that their hospital was doing the right thing for its reputation (Williamson, 2010). Not all conflicts end as well as this; and this one took over 30 years of unremitting effort by patient activists. As in the example in maternity care in Chapter 1, many people – parents, child patients, patient activists, paediatric staff – felt anguish along the way. But it is a good example of patients' emancipation in action.

2. Other emancipation movements show that lifting repression from disadvantaged people, setting them free to contribute to their communities, to the sciences and the arts, may limit opportunities for men and white people through competition for jobs, university places, public attention, and so on. But in the long run setting free the talents of members of oppressed groups enriches society. Women, black people, Asian people and minority ethnic people have made enormous contributions to western societies. Patients include people of all occupations, professions, life experiences, sensibilities, talents, ideas. If they were invited to comment in detail on their recent experiences and impressions, and to identify unnoticed risks or inconspicuous benefits, hospitals and GPs' practices could learn much. Anonymity would be unnecessary, if

patients were welcomed.

3. The idea of emancipation offers a moral purpose for healthcare distinct from market philosophies, from bureaucratic models, and from the institutionalised dominance of any one set of interest-holders. The market with its secrecy, competition, view of patients as commodities costing or earning money, and promotion of greed, is especially ill-suited to patients' care or to health professionals. Bureaucratic power with its layers of oppression is also unsuited. The institutionalised dominance of any one set of interest holders, like that of the medical profession in its golden age, is nowadays out of place. Removing these models (ways of looking at things) and replacing them with a philosophy of equality and inherent human worth could contribute to increases in freedom and in justice.

Medicine can sometimes free patients from illness and from the pains of disability. Emancipating patients from repression, suppression, and oppression could free doctors and managers from the moral and ethical burdens of being oppressors. Healthcare politics would not disappear: they would be better understood and easier to use for good rather than for inadvertent harm.

I like to imagine the health service as a sleigh drawn by three horses in harness abreast, a Russian troika. Health professionals and managers are two of the horses. The third is patients – general patients, patient activists and active patients. Sometimes the other two horses leave the third horse in the corner of a field while they gallop off together. But patients' development of their capabilities, especially in the patients' emancipation movement, shows that the era for excluding the third horse has gone. Even though the horses can sometimes fall out of step with each other, consensuses can keep them together most of the time. The troika must drive along the snowy road in the tall dark forest, out-pacing wolves and robbers, with all three horses in place.

Postscript – the corona virus pandemic

It is too early to say, or even to guess, how the health service will change after the covid-19 pandemic dies down. Signs so far have not been good. Doctors and managers have not included patient groups or patients in their discussions about their plans for their hospitals and general practices, although many patient groups showed that they were eager to contribute (Richards and Scowcroft, 2020). Patients have had to consult their doctors by telephone or video, since going to health service premises has been too risky for both patients and staff. The Secretary of State, Matt Hancock, has declared that most consultations should be electronic from now on (*The Times*. July 31, 2020, p 6). That risks weakening doctor-patient relationships and community links, since they are face-to-face, personal relationships. The new system would change the nature of medical practice, in particular, of general practice, in unpredictable ways (Greenhalgh, 2020). It is a supremely managerial idea, and needs to be discussed thoroughly by patients, doctors, and managers together. Suggestions from Secretaries of State have not always been conspicuously successful; and this one, changing the direction of medical practice instead of building on its strengths, needs to be examined from all perspectives.

References

BJGP - British Journal of General Practice
BMJ - British Medical Journal
JAMA - Journal of the American Medical Association
NEJM - New England Journal of Medicine

Aisenberg N. and Harrington M. (1988) *Women of academe, Outsiders in the sacred grove,* Amherst: The University of Massachusetts Press.

Alford R.R. (1975) *Health care politics, Ideological and interest group barriers to reform,* Chicago: University of Chicago Press.

Arksey H. (1994) 'Expert and lay participation in the construction of medical knowledge', *Sociology of Health & Illness,* vol 16, no 4, pp 448-67.

Baggott R., Allsop J., Jones K. (2005) *Speaking for patients and carers: Health consumer groups and the policy process,* Basingstoke: Palgrave Macmillan.

Baker R. (2020) 'Primary medical care continuity and patient mortality', *BJGP* 2020, vol 70, no 698, p 438.

Barach P. and Phelps G. (2013) 'Clinical sensemaking: a systematic approach to reduce the impact of normalised deviance in the medical profession', *J of the Royal Society of Medicine,* vol 106, no 10, pp 387-90.

Bath M.F., Duncan G.S.J., Gokani V.J. (2017) 'Lay members in the royal colleges: stricter guidelines need to clarify public representation', *J of Health Services Research & Policy,* vol 22, no 1, pp 1-2.

Beard M. (2017) *Women & power, A manifesto,* London: Profile Books.

Beauchamp T.L. and Childress J.F. (2009) *Principles of biomedical ethics,* Oxford: Oxford University Press, seventh edition. First edition 1979.

Beech B. (2011) 'What services to women want and who decides on the kind of care that is offered to them?', in (ed) W. Savage *Birth and power A Savage enquiry revisited,* London: Pinter & Martin Ltd. Pp 179-186, first published in 2007.

Belson P. (2004) 'To get our agenda on other people's agenda', in (eds) H. Curtis and M. Sanderson, *The unsung sixties, Memoirs of social innovation,* London: Whiting and Birch, Ltd., pp 357-70.

Berwick D.M. (2016) 'Era 3 for medicine and health care', *JAMA,* vol 315, no 13, pp 1329-30.

Birthrights. Info@birthrights.org.uk, accessed Jan 2019.

Blackler F. (2006) 'Chief executives and the modernization of the English National Health Service', *Leadership,* vol 2, pp 5-30.

Blennerhassett M. (2008) *Nothing personal, disturbing undercurrents in cancer care,* Oxford: Radcliffe Publishing.

Blomqvist Å. (1991) 'The doctor as double agent: Information asymmetry, health insurance, and medical care', *J of Health Economics,* vol 10, pp 411-32.

Blumenthal D. (1996) 'Quality of health care 1. Quality – what is it?' *NEJM,* vol 335, no 12 pp 891-94.

Bowlby J. (1965) *Child care and the growth of love,* Harmondsworth: Penguin Books, second edition.

Brennan P.A. and Davidson M. (2019) 'Junior doctors have to be able to speak up to improve safety', *BMJ* 2019; 365:l4461.

Brett A.S. and McCullough L.B. (1986) 'When patients request specific interventions', *NEJM,* vol 315, no 21, p 1347-1351.

Bristol Royal Infirmary Inquiry (2001), *Learning from Bristol: The report of the public inquiry into children's heart surgery at the Bristol Royal Infirmary,* 1984-1995, London: Stationery Office.

Brown L. (ed) (1993) *The new shorter Oxford dictionary*, Oxford: Clarendon Press (4th ed.).

Bury M. (2004) 'Researching patient-professional interactions', *J of Health Services Research & Policy*, vol 9, no 1, pp 48-54.

Camus A. (1961) *Resistance, rebellion and death*, NY: Alfred A. Knopf.

Cecil D. (1956) 'Introduction' to Turgenev, *First Love*, London: Hamish Hamilton Ltd. v-x.

Care Quality Commission, *Patient questions*, London: CQC, accessed 23/01/19.

Chandler Harris J. (1886) *Uncle Remus. or Mr Fox, Mr Rabbit, and Mr Terrapin*, London: George Routledge and Sons, Limited.

Checkland K., Harrison S., McDonald R. et al. (2008) 'Biomedicine, holism and general medical practice: responses to the 2004 General Practitioner contract', *Sociology of Health & Illness*, vol 30, no 5, pp 788-803.

Chisholm A., Cairncross L. and Askham J. (2006) *Setting standards, The views of patients, members of the public and doctors on the standards of care and practice they expect of doctors*, Oxford: Picker Institute Europe.

Church J. (2018) 'Quality of life and patient-reported outcomes', *British J of Surgery*, vol 105, no 2, pp 157-158.

Clarke R. (2017) *Your life in my hands, A junior doctor's story*, London: Metro Books.

Cohn S. (2009) 'Where have all the hospital flowers gone?' *BMJ* 2009; 339: b5406.

Coleridge S.T. (1796) from a letter written to John Thelwall In Roc N. *Coleridge and John Thelwall: the road to Nether Stowey*, Humanstier-ebooks.co.uk.

Coulter A. (2002) *The autonomous patient, Ending paternalism in medical care*, London: The Nuffield Trust.

Cumberlege J. (2020) *First do no harm, The report of the independent medicines and medical devices safety review*, London: Her Majesty's Government.

Curtis H. and Sandersen M. (2004) (eds) *The unsung sixties: Memoirs of social innovation*, London: Whiting and Birch Ltd.

Dacre J. (2019) 'Sexism and sexual harassment in the NHS', *BMJ* 2019;367:l6200.

deBronkart D. (2015) 'From patient centered to people powered: autonomy on the rise', *BMJ* 2015; 350: h148.

Department of Health and Social Security (1978) *Report of the committee of inquiry into Normansfield Hospital*, London: HMSO.

Department of Health and Social Security (1983) *NHS management enquiry* (the Griffiths report), London: DHSS.

Dowrick C., Heath I., Hjorleifsson S. et al. (2016) 'Recovering the self: a manifesto for primary care', *BJGP*, vol 66, no 652, pp 582-83.

Duncan P., Cabral C., McCahon D., Guthrie B., Ridd M. J. (2019) 'Efficiency versus thoroughness in medications review: a qualitative interview study in UK primary care', *BJGP* vol 69, no 680, pp 126-134.

Eliot G. (1871-72) *Middlemarch, A study of provincial life,* London: William Blackwood and Sons.

Eliot G. (1999) *Felix Holt, The radical*, London: The Folio Society. First published in 1866.

Eliot T.S. (1936) *Burnt Norton,* in *Four quartets,* London: Faber and Faber.

Elton C. (2019) 'Doctors can't care for patients if the NHS doesn't care for doctors', *BMJ* vol 364, pp 434-36

Entwistle V., Firnigi D., Ryan M., Francis J., Kinghorn P. (2012) 'Which experiences of health care delivery matter to service users and why? A critical interpretative synthesis and conceptual map', *J. Health Services Research & Policy*, vol 17, no 2, pp 70–78.

Epstein R.M. and Street R.L. (2011) 'Shared mind: communication, decision making, and autonomy in serious illness', *The Annals of Family Medicine,* vol 9, no 5, pp 454-461.

Etzioni A. (1961) *A comparative analysis of complex organisations*, New York: Free Press.

Finkelstein D. (2019) 'Truth can only get you so far in politics', *The Times* 16 October, p 23.

Forbes L., Marchand C., Peckham S. (2016) *Review of the quality and outcomes framework in England, Final report,* Policy Research Unit in Commissioning and the Healthcare System: University of Kent.

Freedman L. (1993) 'Book review' in the *Sunday Times Books Supplement* 10 Oct 1993, p 7.

Freidson E. (1970) *Profession of medicine, A study of the sociology of applied knowledge*, New York: Dodd, Mead & Company.

Freidson E. (2001) *Professionalism, The third logic,* Cambridge: Polity Press.

Freud A. (1965) 'Comments' in *The psychoanalytic study of the child*, vol 11, p 432.

Fried C. (1974) *Medical experimentation: Personal integrity and social policy*, New York: American Elsevier.

Fuchs Epstein C. (1988) *Deceptive distinctions: Sex, gender and the political order,* New Haven and London: Yale University Press.

147

Furness P.N. (2003) 'Ethical aspects of histopathology' in (eds) D. Lowe, J. Underwood, *Recent advances in histopathology*, vol 20, London: Royal Society of Medicine Press, pp 115-25.

Garner J. (2019) *How to get the most out of your GP appointment,* accessed 30/01/2019.

General Medical Council (1995) *Good medical practice,* London: GMC.

General Medical Council (1999) *Management in health care; the role of doctors*. London: GMC.

General Medical Council (2012) *Leadership and management for all doctors,* Manchester: GMC.

Gerada C. (2019) 'Doctors and their defence mechanisms', *BMJ* 2019,364: l871.

Gerrard M. (2006) *A stifled voice,* Brighton: Pen Press Publishers Ltd.

Gillespie R. (1997) 'Managers and professionals', in (eds) N. North and Y. Bradshaw *Perspectives in health care,* Basingstoke: Macmillan Press, Ltd., pp 84-109.

Goffman E. (1968) *Asylums, Essays on the social situation of mental patients and other inmates,* Harmondsworth: Penguin Books.

Goldie J. (2014) 'The politics of professionalism in general practice: knowledge is power', *Education for Primary Care,* vol 25, pp 1-2.

Goodrich J. and Cornwell J. (2008) *Seeing the person in the patient,* London: The King's Fund.

Gosport Independent Panel (2018) *Gosport War Memorial Hospital: The report of the Gosport independent panel,* London: HM Government, House of Commons no.1084.

Gray J.A.M. (2002) *The resourceful patient,* Oxford: eRosetta Press.

Greener I., Harrington B.E., Hunter D.J., Mannion R., Powell M. (2014) *Reforming healthcare, What's the evidence?* Bristol: Policy Press.

Greenhalgh T. (2020) 'The UK revolution in primary care', *Quad, Oxford Alumni Magazine*, pp 16-17.

Griffiths R. (1992) 'Seven years of progress - general management in the NHS', *Health Economics*, vol 1, pp 61-70.

Gutstein L. (1993) 'Designed to heal', *Longevity* December 1993, pp 43-47.

Hammond P. (2015) *Staying alive, How to get the best from the NHS*, London: Quercus Publishing Ltd.

Hannan K.L., Campbell S.M., Lester H.E. (2012) 'Patients' views of pay for performance in primary care', *BJGP* 2012; DO1:10.339/bjgp 12X64138.

Harrison S. and McDonald R. (2008) *The politics of healthcare in Britain*, London: SAGE Publications Ltd.

Harrison S. and Smith C. (2004) 'Trust and moral motivation: redundant resources in health and social care?' *Policy & Politics*, vol 32, no 3, pp 371-86.

Harrogate and District NHS Foundation Trust (2017) *Environmental cleanliness, community infection and control, Guidance for general practice*, Harrogate: Harrogate and District NHS Foundation Trust.

Hayden J. and Lakhani M. (2019) 'Lotte Theresa Newman: an appreciation', *BJGP* vol 69, no 685, p 399.

Heath I. (2016) 'Medicine needs an injection of humanity', *BMJ*, 2013;355:i5705.

Heffernan M. (2011) *Wilful blindness, Why we ignore the obvious at our peril*, London: Simon & Schuster.

Heilbrun C.G. (1989) *Writing a woman's life*, London: The Women's Press.

Hine D. (2007) *Principles and paradoxes in modern healthcare: A challenge to professionalism?* London: Nuffield Trust.

Hogg C. (1999) *Patients, power & politics, From patients to citizens,* London: SAGE Publications.

Hogg C. (2009) *Citizens, consumers and the NHS, Capturing voices,* Basingstoke: Palgrave Macmillan.

Hunter D.J. (2006) 'From tribalism to corporatism: the continuing managerial challenge to medical dominance', in (eds) D. Kelleher, J. Gabe, G. Williams, *Challenging medicine,* Abingdon, Oxon: Routledge, second edition, pp 1-23.

Illman J. (2019) 'Michael O'Donnell, obituary', *BMJ* 2019;365:l1896.

Institute of Medicine (2001) *Crossing the quality chasm: a new health system for the 21st century,* Washington DC: National Academy Press.

Irvine D. (2003) *The doctors' tale, Professionalism and public trust,* Abingdon: Radcliffe Medical Press Ltd.

Irvine D. (2017) *Medical professionalism and the public interest: Reflections on a life in medicine,* London: Royal College of General Practitioners Heritage Committee.

Ives J., Papanikitas A., Myres P. and Gregory S. (2018) 'Shared decision-making: a need for honesty?' *BJGP* vol 68, no 671, pp 292-293.

Jefferson M. (2015) *Negroland, a memoir,* London, Granta Books.

Jensen U.F. and Mooney G. (1990) 'Changing values: autonomy and paternalism in medicine and health care' in (eds) U.F. Jensen and G. Mooney, *Changing values in medical and health care decision-making,* Chichester: John Wiley & Sons, pp 1-15.

Jolley M.G. (1988) 'Ethics of cancer management from the patient's perspective', *J of Medical Ethics,* vol 14, no 4, pp 188-190.

Kassirer J.P. (1998) 'Managing care – should we adopt a new ethic?' *NEJM 1998,* vol 339, no 6, pp 397-98.

Kay A. (2017) *This is going to hurt,* London: Picador.

Kennedy I. (1981) *The unmasking of medicine,* London: George Allen & Unwin.

Kennedy I. (2006) *Learning from Bristol: Are we?* London: Healthcare Commission, p 27.

Klein R. (1989) *The politics of the NHS,* Harlow, Essex: Longman second ed., first ed. 1983.

Klein R. and Lewis J. (1976) *The politics of consumer representation, A study of community health councils,* London: Centre for Studies in Social Policy.

Klikauer T. (2015) 'What is managerialism?' *Critical Sociology,* vol 41, no 7-8, pp 1103-19.

Komesaroff P.A., Kerridge I.H., Isaacs D., et al. (2016) 'The scourge of managerialism and the Royal Australian College of Physicians', *Med J Australia,* vol 202, no 19, pp 519-21.

Lack J.A. (2003) 'Chairman's introduction' in (eds) J.A. Lack A-M. Rollin, G. Thoms, L. White, C. Williamson, *Raising the standard: Information for patients,* London: The Royal College of Anaesthetists, The Association of Anaesthetists of Great Britain and Ireland, pp 5-6.

le Carré J. (1974) *Tinker tailor soldier spy,* London: Hodder and Stoughton, Ltd.

Learmonth M. and Harding N. (2004) 'Introduction' to *Unmasking health management: A critical text,* (eds) M. Learmonth and N. Harding, New York: Nova Science Publishers, Inc., pp vii-x.

Lepore J. (2018) *These truths, A history of the United States,* NY, NY: W.W. Norton & Company.

Loughlin M. (2004) 'Orwellian quality: the bosses' revolution', in (eds) M. Learmonth and N. Harding *Unmasking health management – A critical text*, New York: Nova Science Publishers, Inc., pp 25-39.

Lown B.A, Hanson I., and Clark W.D. (2009) 'Mutual influence in shared decision making: a collaborative study of patients and physicians'. *Health Expectations*, vol 12, no 2, pp 160-174

Lown M. and Peters D. (2018) 'Industialised medicine: a step too far?' *BJGP*, vol 68, no 676, pp 543-54.

Lukes S. (2005) *Power: A radical view*, Basingstoke: Palgrave Macmillan, second edition.

Macintyre B. (2018) *The spy and the traitor*, UK: Viking, Penguin Books.

Mandelstam M. (2011) *How we treat the sick, Neglect and abuse in our health services*, London: Jessica Kingsley Publishers.

Mangin D. and Troop L. (2007) 'The quality and outcomes framework: what have you done to yourselves?' *BJGP*, vol 57, no 539, pp 435-37.

Mannion R. and Davies H. (2018) 'Rethinking the relationship between organisational culture and quality of care', *BMJ* 2018;363:k4907.

Mannion R. and Davies H. (2019) 'How to raise and respond to concerns in healthcare settings', *BMJ* 2019;366:l4944.

Mansbridge J. (2001) 'The making of oppositional consciousness' in *Oppositional consciousness, The subjective roots of social protest* (eds) J. Mansbridge and A. Morris, Chicago: The University of Chicago Press, pp 1-9, 15-16.

Martin M. and White L. (2003) 'A review of other resources', in (eds) J.A. Lack et al, *Raising the standard: Information for patients*, London Royal College of Anaesthetists and Association of Anaesthetists of Great Britain and Ireland, pp 136-142.

Martinsons J. (1980) 'The Planetree model: personalised patient care', *Trustee*, September 1980, pp 8-10.

Mayor S. (2018) 'Removing GPs' cash incentives led to 'performance decline'. *BMJ*;362; k3770.

McCartney M. (2012) 'Who do doctors work for?' *J Royal Society of Medicine*, vol 105, pp 189-90.

McCartney M. (2016) 'If staff aren't cared for they can't care for patients', *BMJ* 2016;354:i4690.

McCartney M. (2018) 'What I've learnt in four and a half years', *BMJ*, 2018;362:k3745.

McCoubrey I. (2019) Letter to *The Times* 9 November, p 28.

McMahon B. (2018) 'Oh, could you mansplain again, please?' *times 2*, October 18, pp 1-3.

Mechanic D. (2004) 'In my chosen doctor I trust', *BMJ,* vol 329, pp 1418-19.

Menzies Lyth I. (1988) *Containing anxiety in institutions*, London: Free Associations Books.

Mid Staffordshire NHS Foundation Trust Inquiry (2013) *Independent inquiry into care provided by Mid Staffordshire NHS Foundation Trust, January 2005-March 2009,* Vol I. London: The Stationery Office.

Minchin M., Roland M., Richardson J. et al. (2018) 'Quality of care in the United Kingdom after removal of financial incentives', *NEJM* 2018, vol 379, no 10, pp 948-57.

Misslebrook D. (2001) *Thinking about patients*, Newbury, Berkshire: Libra Pharmaceuticals.

Misselbrook D. (2011) 'The quality and outcomes framework: a critical assessment', in (eds) N. Wald and D. Misselbrook, *The future of prevention in cardiovascular disease,* London: RSM Press, chapter 4.

Montori V. (2017) *Why we revolt, a patient revolution for careful and kind care*, Rochester, Minnesota: The Patient Revolution.

Morrison P. (1994) *Understanding patients*, London: Balliere Tindall.

Murphy-Lawless J. (2016) 'Risk and contingency', *AIMS Journal*, vol 28, no 2, pp 8-10.

Norman A.H., Russell A.J., Merli C. (2016) 'The quality and outcomes framework: body commodification in UK', *Social Science & Medicine,* vol 170, pp 77-80.

O'Mahony S. (2019) *Can medicine be cured? The corruption of a profession,* London: Head of Zeus Ltd.

Oliver D. (2018) 'Moral distress in hospital doctors', *BMJ* 2018;360:k1333.

Oliver S., Milne R., Bradburn J., Buchanan P., Kerridge L., Walley T. and Gabay, J. (2001) 'Involving consumers in the needs-led research programme: a pilot project', *Health Expectations* vol 4, no. 1, pp 18-28.

Parker L., Fabbri A., Grundy Q., et al. (2019) ' "Asset exchange" '- interactions between patient groups and the pharmaceutical industry', *BMJ* 2019;367:l6674.

Parroy S., Thoms G., Williamson C. (2003) 'The practicalities of developing patient information' in (eds) Lack J.A. et al., *Raising the standard: Information for patients*, London RCA and AAGBI, pp 15-23.

Parsons T. (1951 *The social system*, Glencoe, Illinois: Free Press.

Patients Association (2019) *Patient Voice*, Harrow, Middlesex: The Patients Association.

Pellegrino E.D. and Thomasma D.C. (1981) *A philosophical basis of medical practice: Towards a philosophy and ethics of the healing professions*, Oxford: Oxford University Press.

Pereira Gray D., Sidaway-Lee K., White E., Thorne A., Evans P.H. ((2018) 'Continuity of care with doctors – a matter of life and death? A systematic review of continuity of care and mortality', *BMJ Open*, 2018;0: e021161..doi:10.1136/bmjopen--2017-021161.

Picker Institute (2009) *2008-2009 Picker report*, Camden, ME.: Picker Institute.

Picker Institute Europe (2008/9) *When patients' views really count*, Oxford: Picker Institute Europe.

Pratt J. (1995) *Practitioners and practices, a conflict of values?* Oxford: Radcliffe Medical Press.

R.M. (1959) 'Introduction' to *The torrents of spring* by I. Turgenev, translated by D. Magarshack, London: The Folio Society pp 3-6.

Richards N. and Coulter A. (2007) *Is the NHS becoming more patient-centered? Findings from a national survey of NHS patients in England, 2002-07*. Oxford: Picker Institute Europe.

Richards T and Scowcroft H. (2020) 'Patient and public involvement in covid-19 policy making', *BMJ* 2020;370:m2575. (01 July 2020)

Riggare S. (2018) 'The patients of the future are already here', *BMJ* 2018; 360: k846.

Rimmer A. (2019) 'Space to breathe: why we need doctors' messes', *BMJ* 2019;364:k5367.

Robinson J. (2004/5) 'Shooting the messenger', *AIMS Journal,* vol 16, no 4, p 15.

Roland M. (2004) 'Linking physicians' pay to the quality of care - a major experiment in the United Kingdom', *NEJM* 2004, vol 351, no 14, pp 1448-54.

Royal College of Anaethetists and Association of Anaethetists of Great Britain and Ireland (2003), *Anaethesia explained,* London: RCA and AAGB1.

Royal College of General Practitioners (1997) *How to work with your doctor,* Exeter: Royal College of General Practitioners.

Royal College of Physicians (2005) *Doctors in society: Medical professionalism in a changing world,* London: Royal College of Physicians.

Royal Liverpool Children's Inquiry (2001) *The Royal Liverpool children's inquiry report,* London: Stationery Office.

Russell G. (2015) 'Does paying for performance in primary care save lives? Probably not, according to a study of the evidence from the UK', *BMJ* 2015;350:h1051.

Salisbury H. (2019) 'Small is beautiful', *BMJ* 2019;365:l4117.

Savage W. (1986) *A Savage enquiry: who controls childbirth?* London: Virago Press.

Schneider S.H. (2005) *The patient from hell, How I worked with my doctors to get the best of modern medicine and how you can too,* Cambridge, MA: Da Cape Press.

Sen A. (2009) *The idea of justice,* London: Allen Lane.

Sharrock W. and Watson R. (1995) 'The incarnation of social structure' in (ed) P. Joyce *Class,* Oxford: Oxford University Press, pp. 108-113.

Sinclair S. (1997) *Making doctors, an institutional apprenticeship,* Oxford: Berg.

Speirs J. (1995) *The invisible hospital and the secret garden: An insider's commentary on the NHS reforms,* Abingdon: Radcliffe Medical Press.

Starr P. (2000) 'The growth of medical authority' in (ed) P. Brown, *Perspectives in medical sociology,* Long Grove, Illinois: Waveland Press, Inc, pp 557-565.

Stockett K. (2010) *The help,* London: Penguin Books. First published in US in 2009.

Teale K. (2007) 'What's wrong with the wards?' *BMJ,* vol 334, no 7584, p 97.

Turgenev I. (1950) *A sportsman's notebook, 1848-50,* London: The Cresset Press.

Thomas P. (2002) 'The midwife you have called knows you are waiting', *AIMS Journal*, vol 14, no 3, pp 6-8.

Toch H. (1965) *The social psychology of social movements*, Indianapolis, Indiana: The Bobbs - Merrill Company Inc.

Tolstoy L (1925) *War and peace,* London: William Heinemann, Ltd.

Tong R. (1997) *Feminist approaches to bioethics*, Oxford: Westview Press.

Tong R. (2009) *Feminist thought*, Boulder, Colorado: Westview Press.

Wang M. (2007) 'Informing patients a "must" not a "maybe" '. *Bulletin of the Royal College of Anaesthetists,* vol 44, pp 2233 - 35.

Wessely A. and Gerada C. (2013) 'When doctors need treatment: an anthropological approach to why doctors make bad patients', *BMJ* 2013;347:f6644.

Wikipedia (2020) Beecher Stowe H. (1852) *Uncle Tom's cabin, or life among the lowly,* Boston, MA: John P. Jewett & Company.

Williams G. and Popay J. (2006)' Lay knowledge and the privilege of experience', In (eds) L.D. Kellerher et al., *Challenging medicine,* London: Routledge, second edition, pp 122 -145.

Williams H. (2003) 'Registrar's report', *Bulletin of the Royal College of Pathologists,* vol 124, pp 33 -34.

Williamson C. (1985) *Hearing patients' appeals against continued compulsory detention*, Birmingham: National Association of Health Authorities and Trusts, second edition.

Williamson C. (1987) *Reviewing the quality of care in the NHS*, Birmingham: National Association of Health Authorities.

Williamson C (1992) *Whose standards? Consumer and professional standards in health care*, Buckingham: Open University Press.

Williamson C. (1993) 'A model ahead of its time', *BMJ* vol 307, p 742.

Williamson C. (1998) 'The rise of doctor-patient working groups', *BMJ* 1998; 317:1374-77.

Williamson C. (1999a) 'Reflections on healthcare consumerism: insights from feminism'. *Health Expectations,* vol 2, no 3, pp 150-58.

Williamson C. (1999b) 'The challenge of lay partnership', *BMJ,* 319, pp 721-22.

Williamson C. (2000) 'Consumer and professional standards: working towards consensus', *Quality in Health Care,* vol 9, pp 190 – 194.

Williamson C. (2003) 'The patient perspective on information', in (eds) J.A. Lack, A-M. Rollin, G.Thoms , L. White, C. Williamson. C., *Raising the standard: Information for patients*, RCA and AAGBI, pp 73-76.

Williamson C. (2005) 'Withholding policies from patients restricts their autonomy', *BMJ* vol 331, pp 1078-80.

Williamson C. (2007a) 'How do we find the right patients to consult?' *Quality in Primary Care,* vol 15, pp 195-199.

Williamson C. (2007b) 'Lab tests: levelling up or levelling down?' Letter in *The Bulletin of the Royal College of Pathologists*, vol 138, p 63.

Williamson C. (2008) 'Alford's theoretical political framework and its application to interests in health care now', *BJGP*, vol 58, no 552, pp 512-16.

Williamson C. (2010) *Towards the emancipation of patients, Patients' experiences and the patient movement,* Bristol: The Policy Press.

Williamson C. (2011) 'The failure of PPA to define its ideology', in (ed) A. Henderson *Insights from the playgroup movement, Equality and autonomy in a voluntary organisation,* Stoke on Trent: Trentham Books, pp 119-139.

Williamson C. (2015) 'Performance management: can patients' autonomy be protected?' *BJGP* vol 65, no 634, pp 228-229.

Williamson C. (2016) 'Fostering empowerment: ethical, political, and practical considerations', *BJGP*, vol 66, no 652, pp 580-82.

Williamson C. (2017) 'Secrecy and coercion in the QOF: a scandal averted?' *BJGP*, vol 67, no 659, pp 250-51.

Williamson C. (2018a) ' "Real" patients and "real" doctors', *BJGP* vol 68, no. 677, pp 591-92.

Williamson C. (2018b) 'Combining professional and lay knowledge to improve patient care', *BJGP*, vol 68, no 666, pp 39 -40.

Wilson E.O. (1975) *Sociobiology: The new synthesis*, Cambridge MA: The Belknap Press.

Winnicott D.W. (1964) *The child, the family, and the outside world*, Harmondsworth: Penguin Books.

Wood B. (2000) *Patient power? The politics of patients' associations in Britain and America*, Buckingham: Open University Press.

York Teaching Hospital NHS Foundation Trust (2019) *Complaints annual report 2018/19*, York: York Teaching Hospital NHS Foundation Trust.

Young I.M. (1990) *Justice and the politics of difference*, Princeton, NJ: Princeton University Press.

Zakarian B. (1996) *The activist cancer patient, How to take charge of your treatment*, New York: John Wiley & Sons, Inc.

Zinn H. (2010) *A people's history of the United States*, New York: Harper Collins Publishers (first published in 1980).

Index

patients 'as people' or non people, 1,16-17, 19,   135-137
Patients Association, 69, 113
patients' political progress, 111-115
Picker Institute, 45, 114
Planetree Association, 114, 131
power, definition 3, medical power 70, doctor-manager balance 86
Pratt, Julian, 120
pressure groups / patient activist groups 24-25
principles, definition 32, patient principles listed 32, in *Good Medical Practice* 68-69, in *Anaesthesia explained* 75
Quality and Outcomes Framework (QOF), 91-96, 103-104
RAGE, Radiation Action Group Exposure, 29
rationing, 99, 120
rhetoric, 9, 132
Riggare, Sara, 51-53
Rollin, Anna-Maria, 72
Royal College of Anaesthetists, 71
Royal College of General Practitioners, 18, 46, 59, 63, 67, 93, 95
Royal College of Physicians, 117
Savage, Wendy, 64, 69
Schneider, Stephen, 51-53
Sen, Amartya, and theory, vii, 40
Seymour, Ann, 72
Shinman, Sheila, 120
Smith, Andrew, 62-64, 72
social action, 24
social structures, definition 3,

constraints and opportunities 28, influence 54, lack of 113
standards, definition 28, and CHCs 66, and medical royal colleges 67, categories, 125-127, breaches 125, 134-135
stress, of doctor-patient activist work 74-75
Thatcher, Margaret, 122
Thoms, Gavin, 72
Toch, Hans, 23
Wang, Madeleine, 72
White, Lucy, 72
wilful blindness, 63
Wilkie, Patricia, 61, 70, 72
Williams, Helen, 62- 64
Williamson, Charlotte, 72
Winnicott, Donald W, 27
women's movement, 8-13, 49
Young, Iris Marion, and theory, 41
Zakarian, Beverly, 51- 54

Quacks, founded in 1703